Exploring Calculus and Differential Equations
with the
TI-89 and TI-92 PLUS

Michael B. Schneider
Southwestern Illinois College

Lawrence G. Gilligan
College of Applied Science, University of Cincinnati

D1571618

GILMAR Publishing
P.O. Box 6376
Cincinnati, OH 45206
(513) 751-8688

http://www.gilmarpublishing.com

Printed in the United States of America

ISBN: 1-888808-05-5

This learning package (of text and files) is available in two
formats:

1) Traditional text plus diskette of files
                    or
2) Totally electronically (download from http://www.mathware.com)

Cover design: Patricia Lloyd
Printing: United Graphics

The TI-89 and TI-92 Plus Module are products of Texas
Instruments Incorporated. TI-Graph Link is a trademark of Texas
Instruments Incorporated.

GILMAR Publishing
P.O. Box 6376
Cincinnati, OH 45206
(513) 751-8688

email: gilmar2000@yahoo.com   web: http://www.gilmarpublishing.com

CONTENTS

This book is dedicated to

Jane, John, Mike

and

Dr. Theron Rockhill, Calculus Professor Extraordinaire

Preface

About the collection of files

There are over 65 files accompanying this text and they provide the basis for this project. These files are program and utility files, text files, and function files. They are grouped into one large file which you will need to download to your calculator. If you have a TI-89, use the grouped file CALC.89g and if you have a TI-92 PLUS, use the grouped file CALC.9xg.

You will need a TI-Graph Link® cable and the appropriate accompanying software. (The software is downloadable from TI's website. As of this writing, the address from which you can select the appropriate file is http://www.ti.com/calc/docs/link.htm.)

You should make a new folder on your hard drive for the TI files you will use. Suppose you create a file called c:calcbook and you have a TI-89. Copy CALC.89g into that folder from the accompanying diskette. Now run TI Graph Link 89 (be sure your cable is attached and the correct communications port is chosen in the Link menu). Click on "Link" then click on "Send." Next, select the file CALC.89g and then click on the word "Add"; your screen should look like the one below just before you click on "OK."

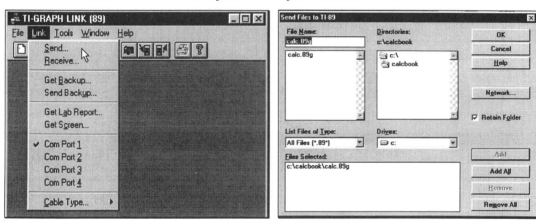

The files should now be transferred to the main folder of your calculator. (Of course, if you have a TI-92 PLUS, you will have to adjust these directions to use the correct filename, CALC.9xg.)

A Note on Using this Book

It may be you are using this book primarily as a help in using your TI-89 or TI-92 PLUS. If that is the case, you may want to give the Overview (pages 1-30) a careful look -- with calculator in hand -- to see how to navigate through the machine's features.[1]

On the other hand, perhaps you are using this book to aid in your course work in a calculus course or in differential equations. In that case, you will find that the explorations

---

[1] We tried to cover most of the features that are common to both the TI-89 and TI-92 PLUS. One unique TI-92 PLUS feature is the geometry screen and that is not covered in this text. Interested readers should consult their accompanying manual or try referencing the book *Mastering the TI-92: Explorations from Algebra Through Calculus* by N. Rich, J. Rose, and L. Gilligan (GILMAR, 1996).

are useful to you. We tried to order these explorations in an order similar to that which you will encounter in your coursework. The topics of the explorations are consistent with the topics in many courses in calculus and differential equations.

Viewing/Editing Programs vs. Running Programs

Running a program is easy -- you simply type the name of the program on the edit line followed by a set of parentheses. The parentheses may contain parameters (separated by commas) or not, depending on the way the program is written. We walk you through that syntax as carefully as we can in the text but you may want to use the Program Listing feature of the book (pages 109-115) to see what, if any, parameters are necessary for a particular function or program.

Several programs on the accompanying diskette are programs that provide menus from which to choose other programs or functions.

Most of the time we envision users of this text to use the programs. Sometimes you may want to write a routine for your own needs. Editing and creating programs occurs in the program editor, accessible only through the APPS key. Of course, this assumes a knowledge of programming expertise but we encourage the savvy reader to pursue program writing to solve problems they encounter in their coursework.

Acknowledgments

The foresight Texas Instruments had to develop such a marvelous, portable computer algebra system is noteworthy and the cooperation of several people there has been invaluable. In particular, we are indebted to Gosia Brothers, Yong Cui, Michelle Miller, Glen Thornton , and Scott L. Webb and for their encouragement and support. David Stoutemyer provided the code for the polycoef and polydeg functions and we relish our professional relationship with him over the years.

As always, thanks to Patricia Lloyd for her talents on the cover design.

An Overview of the TI-89 and TI-92 PLUS

The MODE Key

There are three pages of choices for the mode settings which control how algebraic expressions, numbers, matrices and graphs are displayed and interpreted. The three pages along with the default settings are shown below:

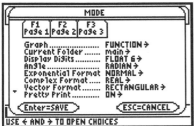  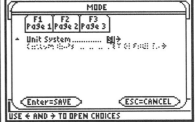

To change a setting, simply cursor down to it and press the right cursor key to choose from a list of options for that particular item.

For example, to split the screen into two parts vertically, on page 2[2] we change the settings to:

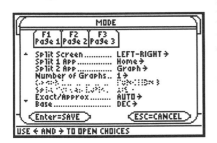

Left: Choose "LEFT-RIGHT" for the screen split. We also chose the left-hand split ("Split 1 App") to be the home screen and the right side split to be the graph window. Press ENTER to save the changes. Right: The home screen is on the left and the graph screen is on the right.

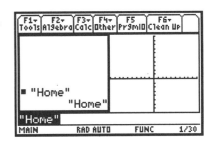

To see how the mode settings can affect the appearance of numerical results, we will return the screen to "FULL" and display the output of the calculation $\frac{1}{8}+\frac{4}{7}$ three ways.

TIPS!
1. Always stay in "AUTO" mode.
2. When you press the ENTER key, you will get an exact answer, if the calculator is capable of finding it. When you press the ◆ ENTER keys, you will get an *approximate* answer!

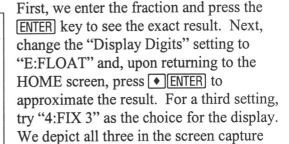

First, we enter the fraction and press the ENTER key to see the exact result. Next, change the "Display Digits" setting to "E:FLOAT" and, upon returning to the HOME screen, press ◆ ENTER to approximate the result. For a third setting, try "4:FIX 3" as the choice for the display. We depict all three in the screen capture below:

---

[2] Reach page 2 by pressing F2 after pressing the MODE key

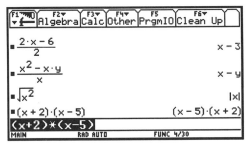

In "FLOAT" mode, $\frac{1}{8}+\frac{4}{7}$ is displayed as .696428571429; in "FIX 3" mode, it is .696.

Another TIP!
When there are lots of items in a list from which to choose (such as the 25 alternatives in the "Display Digits" menu), select an item by pressing its first character code. To choose "E:FLOAT" for example, press
[ALPHA] [E]. It is not necessary to cursor down to your choice.

Algebra on the HOME Screen

The power of these calculators is their ability to do symbolic manipulation. Expressions will be simplified, if possible, when entered and we show a screen below with several algebraic entries.

Notice that the product $(x+2)(x-5)$ does not automatically get expanded. To expand or factor expressions or solve equations, we invoke the "[F2] Algebra" menu.

Another TIP!
To clear the home screen, press [F1] and then choose "8:Clear home". Press the [CLEAR] key to clear all entries to the right of the cursor on the edit line. (If the cursor is all the way to the right, the entire line is cleared.)

There are eleven options under the "Algebra" menu. Notice how factor and cfactor (for factoring over the complex numbers) differ.

There is a lot of versatility in the algebra commands. "Solve(" for example can be used to solve an equation for a specific variable. "Expand(" can be used to write a fraction as a sum of two or more fractions (called *partial fraction decomposition*) and "Zeros(" returns a list of zeros of an expression. See the screen below for specific examples.

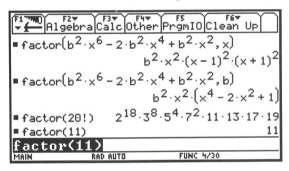

Some additional algebra command examples.

The factor command can yield different results depending upon the variable you want to factor with respect to. The first two lines of the screen below differ only by first factoring with respect to x and then with respect to b. The other two lines are there to show you can factor numbers, too. (If the number is returned, it is a prime number.)

There are other algebra commands. "comDenom(" will return a reduced fraction with one numerator and one denominator. "propFrac(" returns a proper fraction and "cZeros(" returns a list of complex zeros for an expression.

The screen below illustrates these commands.

 More Tips!
1. Beware of implicit multiplication! While $2x$ is understood to mean 2 times x, the expression xy represents a single variable with a two-letter name. To enter $x*y$ you need to use the multiplication key (or the space bar) between x and y.
2. After a while, you may want to use letters that have been previously assigned. The convenient F6 key clears out single letter variable names.
3. The previous line's output can be accessed without retyping it – simply press 2nd [ANS]!

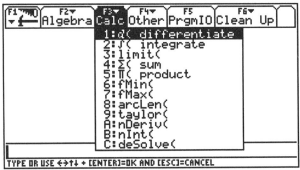

The reader is urged to experiment with these commands as well as those not listed here.

Calculus on the HOME Screen

There are twelve commands available from the [F3] menu; they are displayed below[3]:

To illustrate the "differentiate" command, we find three derivatives in the screen below. The first is the derivative with respect to x) of the function $f(x) = 2x^3 - \dfrac{5}{x}$; the second example is the partial derivative with respect to x of the function $g(x) = x^2 y - \cos(x + 2y)$; and the third example is the second derivative of x^3, $\dfrac{d^2}{dx^2}(x^3)$:

---

[3] The symbols for differentiating and integrating also have keyboard shortcuts. The derivative symbol is the second function of the numeric "8" key and the integral is the second function of the "7" key.

We also provide three examples of the integration command. For the first example, we find the (indefinite) integral of $4 - x^2$. (Notice that the constant of integration "+ c" is omitted.) Then we find the definite integral $\int_{-2}^{2} \left(4 - x^2\right) dx$. The third example in the screen below is a multiple integral which is evaluated by embedding integral symbols:

If you'd like to see the "+C" for the constant of integration, it can be done by entering $\int$(4-x^2,x,c) provided there is nothing stored in the memory location C.

Several screens for the remaining calculus commands appear below.

The limit command can used to find 2-sided limits, left-hand limits or right-hand limits.

Sums and products can be either finite or infinite.

A function's maximum (fMax) or minimum (fMin) location can be found. Below, we find the minimum for the defined function.

An *x* value of 1.2868 is returned but in order to find the function's minimum value, we must evaluate the function there.

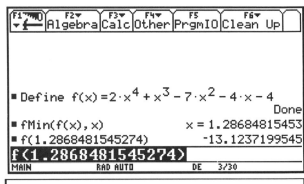

Two examples of finding the length of arc:

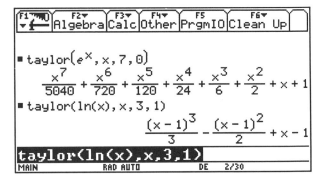

The seventh degree Taylor polynomial approximation for $y = e^x$ about $x = 0$ (Maclaurin) is computed. Also, the third degree Taylor polynomial approximation for $y = \ln x$ about $x = 1$ is displayed.

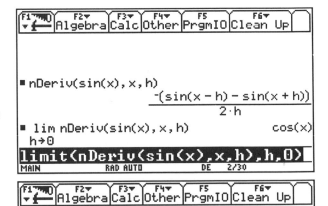

The "nDeriv(" command uses the central difference quotient formula $\dfrac{f(x+h) - f(x-h)}{2h}$ to approximate the numerical value of the first derivative at *x*. If we did not include the "*h*", the default numerical value of .001 is computed. Of course, *h* must not be currently in use.

You may be more familiar with the standard *difference quotient* (sometimes called the *forward difference quotient*), $\dfrac{f(x+h) - f(x)}{h}$. This is called "avgRC" (for average rate of change) and can be found in the catalog.

The "deSolve(" command is explained in depth in the differential equation explorations later in this text. For now, suffice it to say that most first-order and second-order ordinary differential equations (either with initial conditions or not) can be solved with this command. Four examples appear on the screen below:

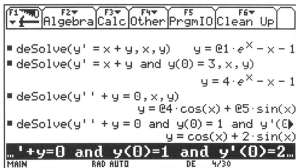

The @1 symbol represents an arbitrary constant and may be different (@5, @70, etc) on your display.

The first two entries are first order differential equations and the last two are second order DE's.

Graphing

In order to graph functions of a single independent variable it is wise to get familiar with the Y= editor, the WINDOW editor, and the graph window. These are labeled in green (in conjunction with the ◆ key). The first function we will graph is $f(x) = (x+2)(x-1)^2$. To enter it, enter the Y= editor, press ENTER and type in the expression $(x+2)*(x-1)^2$.

Now enter the WINDOW editor and set the values to their default settings by pressing F2 and then choose "6:ZoomStd".

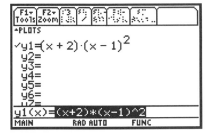
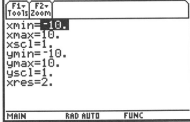
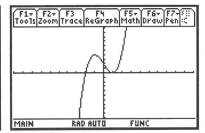

Step 1: Enter the function.   Step 2: Choose WINDOW values.   Step 3: Graph the function.

Before graphing additional functions or examining different window settings, we mention here that the graph screen can be formatted for different appearances. To see the format options, press F1 and choose "9:Format." You should see these possible format options:

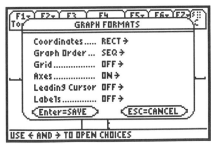

To add a grid, for example, select "Grid" and choose "ON." After pressing ENTER to save the change, revisit the graph screen. You should see a graph paper-like grid.

In addition to formatting options, you can also select the style of the graph. This is done from the Y= editor. With the function to be styled highlighted, press F6. Choose "4:Thick" and observe the graph now. We show it below with the grid on:

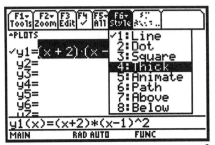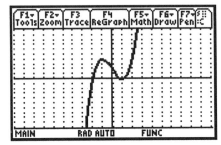

The graph of $f(x) = (x+2)(x-1)^2$ with a thick style and "Grid" turned on.

By the way, now that the function $f(x) = (x+2)(x-1)^2$ is defined in the Y= editor, it can be used from other areas of the calculator. For example, we could find the function's zeros from the HOME screen or even evaluate $f(2)$. You have to use its designation, $y1(x)$, however, in either case. We perform those two operations below:

$$\blacksquare \texttt{zeros(y1(x), x)} \qquad \{\text{-2} \quad 1\}$$
$$\blacksquare \texttt{y1(2)} \qquad\qquad\qquad 4$$

We now present a second graphing example, $f(x) = 3\sin(2x)$. It is entered as $y2(x)$ in the Y= editor. To be sure we **only** see the graph of $y2(x) = 3\sin(2x)$, we "uncheck" $y1(x)$ by pressing F4 when $y1$ is highlighted.

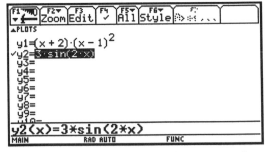

Next, we decide to split the screen vertically in a 1:1 ratio. Also, there is a built in ZoomTrig collection of WINDOW settings. This is obtained by pressing F2 (for the Zoom menu) and then "7:ZoomTrig" from the Y= editor, the WINDOW editor, or the graph screen.

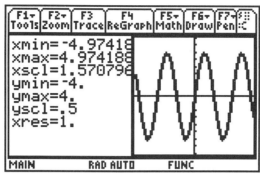

$y = 3\sin(2x)$ after a ZoomTrig

Algebra and Calculus on the Graphing Screen

Once you have a graph displayed, the Math menu ([F5]) provides you with twelve commands. Each command can be used directly on the graph.

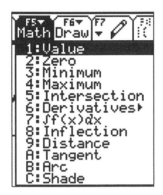

For example, an interesting challenge is to approximate graphically the solutions of the equation $(x+2)(x-1)^2 = 3\sin(2x)$ or, in the language of the calculator, solve $y1(x) = y2(x)$ for x. To do this, we re-select $y1(x)$ and examine the graph of both functions. Next, we invoke the [F5] Math menu and select "5:Intersection" from the list. Since there are three intersections, we will only find one here, the only negative solution. See the screens below:

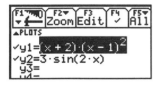
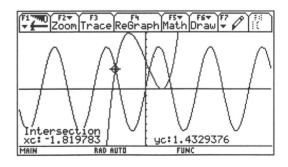

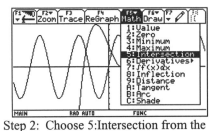

Step 1: Be sure both functions are selected ([F4]).

Step 2: Choose 5:Intersection from the [F5] menu. You will then be prompted to indicate the functions and then a lower bound and an upper bound for the point of intersection.

Step 3. The intersection is approximated. A solution to $(x+2)(x-1)^2 = 3\sin(2x)$ is $x \approx -1.819783$

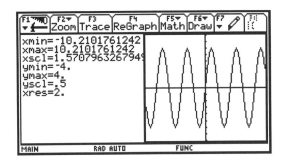

Another TIP!
On a split screen, the [2nd][APPS] key toggles from one of the split screens to the other. Its icon is [⊞].

Alternatively, we could have solved for *x* on the HOME screen.

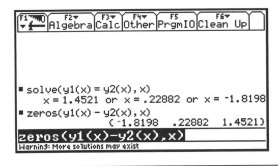

The reader should realize that the following three statements are equivalent:
1. The value *x* is the abscissa of the point of intersection of the graphs of $y = y1(x)$ and $y = y2(x)$.
2. The value *x* is the solution to the equation $y1(x) = y2(x)$.
3. The value *x* is a zero of the expression $y1(x) - y2(x)$.

Additional Editing TIPS!

1. The backspace key, [←], deletes the character to the *left* of the cursor. Often, [♦][←] is more convenient – it deletes the character to the *right* of the cursor.
2. Instead of searching various menus for a particular function or command, it may be easier to use the [CATALOG]. Once it is selected, press the first letter of the command to index to that portion of the catalog.
3. If an item in a pull-down menu has a ▶ to its right, then that item has a submenu.
4. To recall a previous entry, press [2nd][ENTRY]. Press it twice to recall the second past entry, etc.

Option "A: Tangent" in the Math menu ([F5]) computes the equation of the tangent line drawn to a function at a particular point. To access this option, have a function entered in the Y= editor. We have entered $y1(x) = 1 + 4x - x^3$ and we want to find the equation of the line drawn tangent to that curve at $x = 1.5$. When prompted for the *x* value, we can either enter it from the keyboard (preferred method) or trace to that point (or as close as pixel breaks will allow). The resulting screen is shown below:

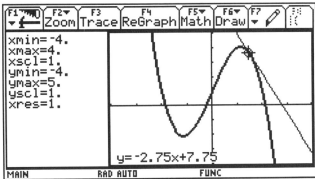

Here, we have split a TI-92+ screen in a 1:2 ratio. A TI-89 can only be split with a 1:1 ratio.

Another calculus application from the Math menu ([F5]) is "7: $\int f(x)dx$ " which finds the area between the positive function f and the x axis. For $y = \sin(x)$, we calculate

$$\int_{0}^{\pi} \sin(x)\,dx$$ witnessed in the screen captures below:

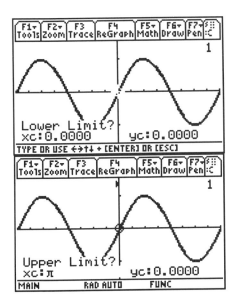

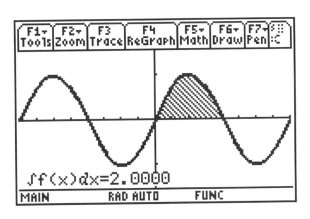

Left: We enter the lower limit (0) and the upper limit (π). Right: The area is computed and shaded.

To find points of inflection from the graphing screen, we choose "8:Inflection" from the [F5] Math menu. For an example, we have chosen the function $y1(x) = x^4 - 2x^2$. Its graph along with some suitable window values are shown below:

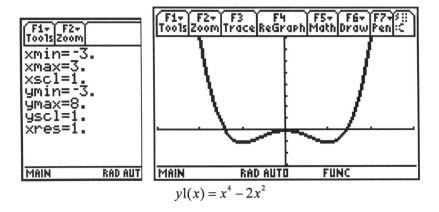

$$yl(x) = x^4 - 2x^2$$

When we choose the points of inflection option from the F5 Math menu, we are prompted for a lower bound and then an upper bound. We can see that there is an inflection point between -1 and 0 so we enter those values for the bounds.

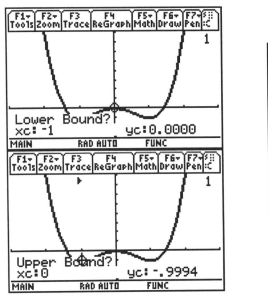
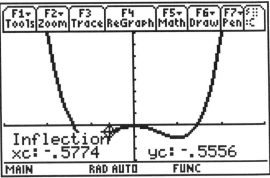

Left: We enter the lower bound (-1) and the upper bound (0). Right: The inflection point is computed and located as $(-.5774, -.5556)$. By symmetry for the curve $yl(x) = x^4 - 2x^2$, a second point of inflection occurs at $(.5774, -.5556)$.

Of course, we could have calculated the point of inflection on the HOME screen as well by finding the zeros of the second derivative as can be seen in the screens below:

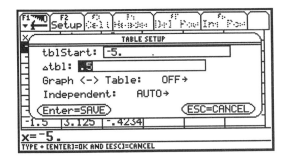

Left: The zeros of the second derivative are $\pm \dfrac{\sqrt{3}}{3} \approx \pm.5774$. Right: The y values are both calculated as $-\dfrac{5}{9}$.

Tables

To display a table of numerical values that represent points on graphs, we begin by setting up the table parameters by pressing ◆[TblSet] . Two important values have to be put into the table: a starting x value (labeled tblStart) and an x-increment (labeled as Δtbl). In the Y= editor, we will be sure $y1(x)$ and $y2(x)$ are both selected. Next, we choose to start the table at $x = -5$ and increment the x values by 0.5. We display the table setup screen and the table of values below:

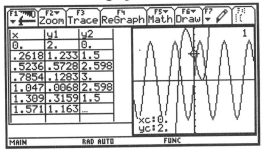

A popular option is to set the Graph <-> Table switch to "ON" so that then the x values correspond to pixel breaks on the graph (the values that get traced). We depict that option in a split screen so the table and the graphs are visible.

> ### *Additional Graphing TIPS!*
> 1. To stop a function from being graphed, press the ON key.
> 2. To pause a function while it is being graphed, press the ENTER key; Press it again to resume graphing.

The Data/Matrix Editor

The Data/Matrix editor is used to enter and operate on lists, matrices, and sets of data. We begin by examining the data of five milestone closings of the Dow Jones Industrial Average (DJIA). To enter the data below, press the APPS key and choose item "6:Data/Matrix Editor." Then select "3:New" and give the data set the name DJIA

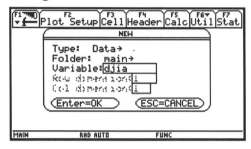

The data is given below"

Date	Coded Date	DJIA
	(in years since 1/1/1906)	
	x values entered in $c1$	Y values entered in $c2$
Nov. 14, 1972	66.9	1003
Jan. 8, 1987	81.1	2002
April 7, 1991	85.3	3004
Feb. 23, 1995	89.2	4003
Nov. 21, 1995	89.9	5000

The date information is placed into column c1 and the DJIA is in c2. It is optional to label the columns at the very top cell. We show the entered data below:

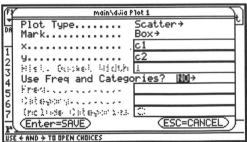

Is the data linear? quadratic? exponential? The best way to answer that question is to examine a plot of the data. To do this, we choose F2 for Plot Setup, then F1 to define Plot #1. See the screen below:

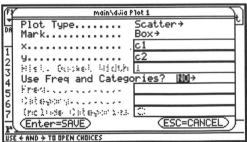

We examine a plot of the data but first, we adjust the WINDOW values.

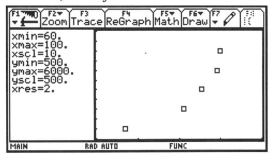

It appears the data is exponential. If you re-enter the data screen ([APPS], "6:Data/Matrix Editor", "1:Current") and type [F5] to calculate, we can find an exponential equation of best fit. See how we selected the parameters in the screen below:

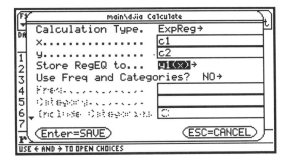

Notice that we have decided to store the equation in $y1(x)$.

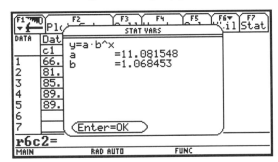

Finally, the exponential regression function, $y1(x) = 11.081548 \cdot 1.068453^x$ is graphed along with the scatter plot of the data in the screen below:

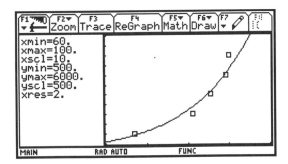

Additional Types of Graphs

In addition to typing functions in one variable, there are five other modes from which to choose: PARAMETRIC, POLAR, SEQUENCE, 3D, and DIFF EQUATIONS. We provide some sample graphs of each in the pages that follow.

Graphing Parametric Equations

We begin by selecting "2:PARAMETRIC" option from the Graph choices on the MODE screen.

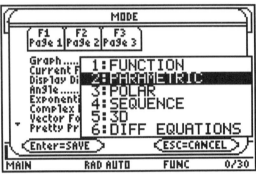

Now consider the following problem. If a ball is thrown with an initial velocity of 80 ft/sec at an angle of 40^0 to the ground, its horizontal component, $x(t)$, and its vertical component, $y(t)$, can be expressed in terms of the parameter t (for time). We enter in the Y = editor the functions $x(t) = 80t\cos(40°)$ and $y(t) = 80t\sin(40°) - 16t^2$. They are displayed along with some window values below:

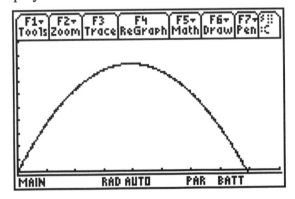

The resulting graph is displayed below:

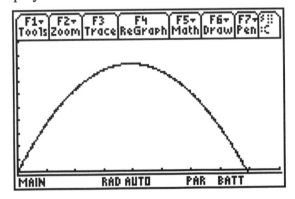

We point out that the graph styles of "Animate" and "Path" are often good choices for parametric equations. We depict six screen captured from graphing with the "Path" style.

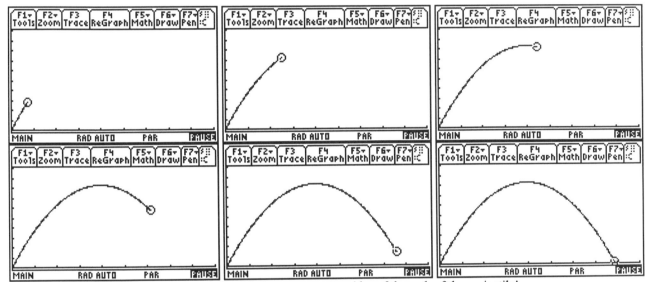

With the graph style "path" chosen, we get an idea of the path of the projectile!
Remember, the drawing of a graph can be paused (as above) by pressing the [ENTER] key. Drawing can be halted by pressing the [ON] key.

Graphing Polar Equations

By choosing the graph type to be "3:POLAR" on the [MODE] screen, we can graph polar equations of the form $r = f(\theta)$.

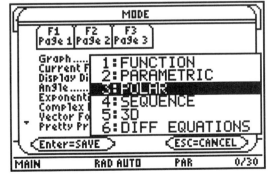

For our first polar example, we enter the function $r1 = 3\cos(2\theta)$ in the Y = editor. With the window values set as below, the following graph should appear.

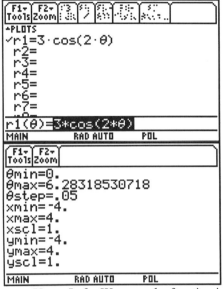

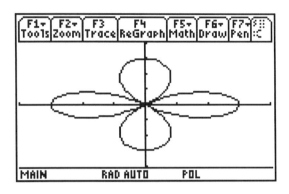

Upper Left: We enter the function in the Y= editor and use the window values in the lower left.

Right: The graph of $r1 = 3\cos(2\theta)$.

The graph is distorted because the scaling on the vertical and horizontal axes is different. That can be fixed by performing a ZoomSqr operation:

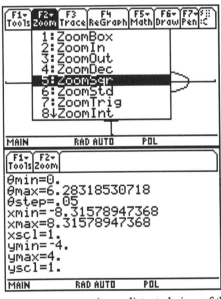

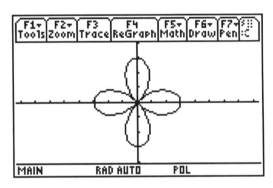

An undistorted view of the graph $r1 = 3\cos(2\theta)$, a rose with four petals.

By default, the coordinates displayed when tracing a polar curve are a point's x and y coordinates. That can be changed in the format dialog box. See the graph of the polar function $r1 = 3.5\cos(4\theta)$ below:

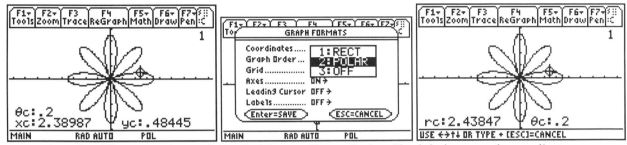

Left: Select F3 Trace and enter .2 (for θ). The coordinates displayed by default are x and y coordinates.
Center: Select the format dialog box by pressing ◆ F and change the coordinates from rectangular to polar.
Right: The polar coordinates are displayed.

As a final look at polar graphing we point out that the curve's resolution is really determined by the window variable θStep. The smaller θStep is, the more refined the graph will be (at the expense of speed, of course). For faster, "rougher" graphs, a larger value of θStep can be used. Compare the two sets of screen captures below for the function $r1 = 4\sin(3\theta)$.

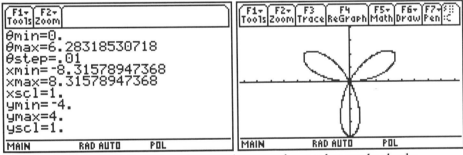

A value of .01 for θStep gives a rather smooth curve but graphs slowly.

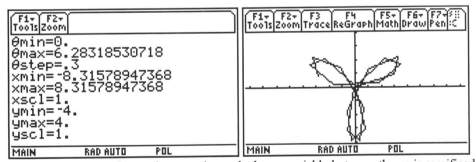

With a value of .3 for θStep, the curve is graphed more quickly but smoothness is sacrificed.

Graphing Sequences

By selecting "4:SEQUENCE" from the $\boxed{\text{MODE}}$ screen, we can graph sequences and partial sums of sequences.

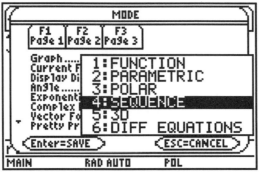

In this mode, the Y= editor allows us to enter sequences (as $u1$, $u2$, etc.) and initial values of sequences ($ui1$, $ui2$, etc.). For a first example, we consider the sequence $u1(n) = 1, \frac{1}{4}, \frac{1}{9}, \ldots, \frac{1}{n^2}$. We enter $u1(n)$ as $1 \div n^2$ and also enter "1" (although it is optional) for the initial value $ui1$. To also examine the sequence of partial sums of the $u1(n)$ sequence, we enter $\sum_{k=1}^{n} \frac{1}{k^2}$ for $u2(n)$. See the screens below.

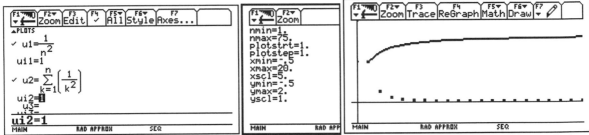

We chose to graph $u1(n)$ in "square" style and $u2(n)$ in "thick" style. The horizontal axis is n and the vertical axis is u.

If we trace to the last value of n (nmax = 75)[4], we can see that

$$u2(75) = \sum_{k=1}^{75} \frac{1}{k^2} \approx 1.631689.$$

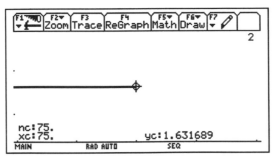

$\sum_{k=1}^{75} \frac{1}{k^2} \approx 1.631689$. It can be shown in calculus that the *exact* value of $\sum_{k=1}^{\infty} \frac{1}{k^2} = \frac{\pi^2}{6} \approx 1.64493406685$.

---

[4] Just press 75 $\boxed{\text{ENTER}}$ after pressing $\boxed{\text{F3}}$ Trace.

For a second example, we will examine a sequence function that is defined ***recursively***. That is, a sequence defined in terms of itself. We entered the function $u1(n) = \cos\big(u1(n-1)\big)$ and $ui1 = 0$. This sequence is: $\cos(0),\ \cos(\cos(0)),\ \cos(\cos(\cos(0))),\ \cos(\cos(\cos(\cos(0)))),\dots$ The screens below show the setup to determine how compositions of the cosine function converge.

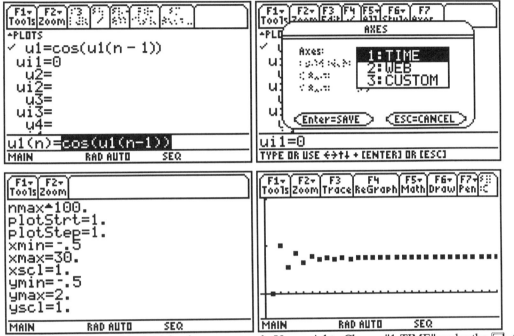

Upper left: The function and its initial value are entered. Upper right: Choose "1:TIME" under the [F7] Axes option.
Lower left: Window values   Lower right: The first 30 entries of the sequence.

To approximate the value to which the terms seem to be converging, we use the [F3] TRACE option. The figure below shows that value to be about 0.739085.

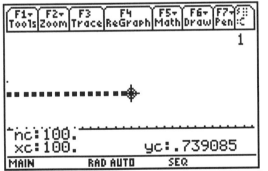

After selecting TRACE, enter 100 and press [ENTER] twice.

An interesting variation of sequence graphing is something called a WEB plot. A WEB plot graphs the sequence by using $u1(n)$ for the vertical axis and $u1(n-1)$ values for the horizontal axis. If a sequence converges to one specific value, as we have in our example, the WEB plot should converge to that point.

To enter a WEB plot, from the Y= editor, select ⌨ Axes. For "Axes:" choose WEB and for "Build Web:" select TRACE.

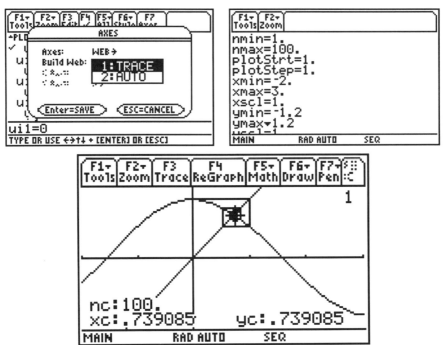

The web is constructed as you TRACE by repeated pressing the right cursor key.

3D Graphing

The 3D graphing mode is used for viewing the graph of a function of two independent variables, $z = f(x,y)$. As with the other graphing types, choose the 3D graph type from the ⌨MODE⌨ screen.

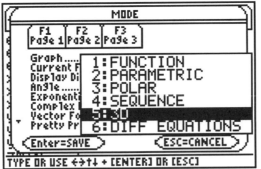

The window parameters are more complicated for 3D graphing and we delineate them below:

```
┌─────┬─────┐
│ F1┬ │ F2┬ │
│Tools│Zoom │
├─────┴─────┴──────┐
│eyeθ=20.          │
│eye∳=70.          │
│eyeψ=10.          │
│xmin=-10.         │
│xmax=10.          │
│xgrid=14.         │
│ymin=-10.         │
│ymax=10.          │
│ygrid▾14.         │
│zmin=-10.         │
│zmax=10.          │
│ncontour=5.       │
├──────────────────┤
│MAIN       RAD AUTO│
└──────────────────┘
```

eyeθ is the rotation angle of the eye from the x axis (if θ is 0, the line of sight is on the xz plane)
eyeφ is the angle of tilt from the positive z axis (if φ is 90°, the eye is on the xy plane)
eyeψ is the angle of counterclockwise rotation around the line of sight set by eyeθ and eyeφ
xgrid is the number of coordinates evaluated between xmin and xmax
ygrid is the number of coordinates evaluated between ymin and ymax
ncontour is the number of contours that will be evenly distributed vertically
xmin, xmax, ymin, ymax, zmin, zmax are self-explanatory

Consider the function $z = 10e^{-x^2 - 0.5y^2}$. We display the graph with two different formats, hidden surface and wire frame.

```
┌─────┬─────┐
│ F1┬ │ F2┬ │
│Tools│Zoom │
├─────┴─────┴──────┐
│eye0=20.          │
│eye∳=70.          │
│eyeψ=10.          │
│xmin=-4.          │
│xmax=4.           │
│xgrid=14.         │
│ymin=-4.          │
│ymax=4.           │
│ygrid=14.         │
│zmin=-5.          │
│zmax=10.          │
│ncontour=5.       │
├──────────────────┤
│MAIN       RAD AUTO│
└──────────────────┘
```

$z = 10e^{-x^2 - 0.5y^2}$

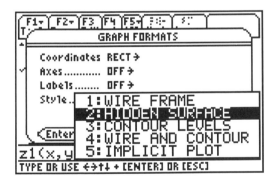

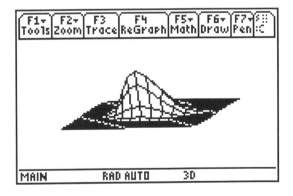

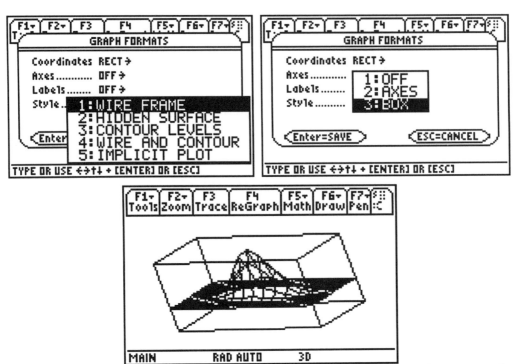

The function is now drawn in wire frame format in a box; the same window values were used.

Finally, we mention that 3D graphs can be animated by rotating using the cursor keys. As the curve is rotated, the three eye values (eyeθ, eyeφ, and eyeψ) change. Two different such views are shown below along with the line of sight values from the window editor.

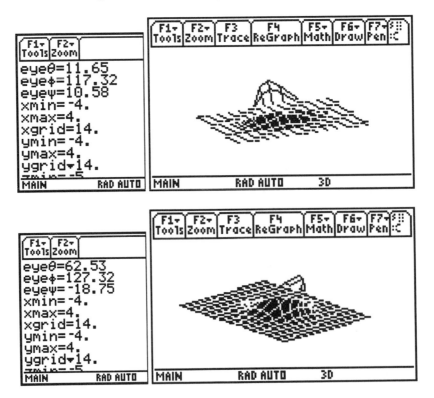

Graphing Solutions to Differential Equations

The last type of graph we can access is the DIFFERENTIAL EQUATIONS option type from the MODE screen.

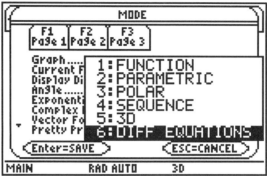

For an example of graphing a solution to a first order differential equation, consider the (non-linear) Bernoulli equation $\dfrac{dy}{dt} = ty^2 - \dfrac{1}{t}y$ with the initial condition $y(1) = 2$. The function is entered in the Y= editor with the window parameters shown below.

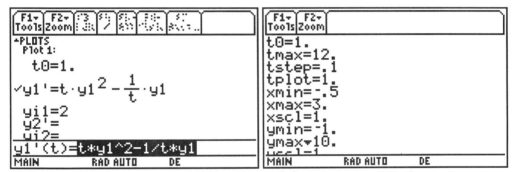

Left: The initial t value is $t_0 = 1$ and $y(t_0) = 2$. Right: Window values.

The solution is shown below:

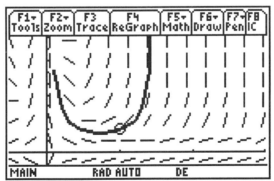

Although this is strictly a numerical approach to solving the differential equation, it can be shown that the solution is $y(t) = \dfrac{-2}{t(2t-3)}$. The dashes represent the slope field option found under format.

To solve the second order differential equation $y'' = -y$ with $y(0) = 0$ and $y'(0) = 1$ we need to establish $y2$ as the derivative of $y1$ so that the derivative of $y2$ is the second derivative of $y1$.

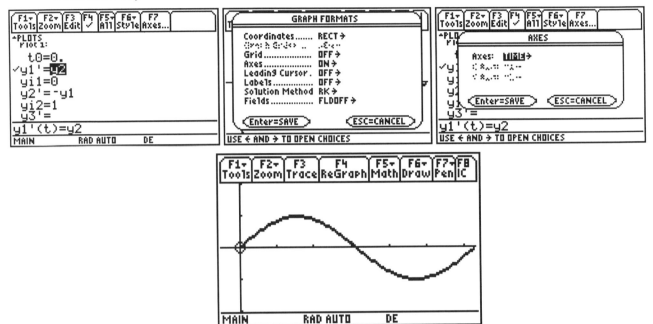

The setup for a second order differential equation is displayed. It should be no surprise that the solution is $y = \sin x$, a function which is the negative of its second derivative.

> ## A Graphing Precaution!
> If you get an **undefined variable** error message when trying to graph, it is often because you have an old data plot still selected in the Y= editor. Simply deselect that plot (highlight it and press [F4]) and your graph should appear.

The Numeric Solver

Although the solve(command does an excellent job in solving many equations, there are equations that have no closed form, exact solutions. In such cases, we can only approximate solutions and we could opt to do that with a graphical approach or we could use the numeric solver. It is available as the last option from the [APPS] key.

Consider the equation $x^{5/3} = \sin(x)$. Before we try to solve it, we graph the two equations $y = x^{5/3}$ and $y = \sin(x)$ in order to get a sense of approximately where solutions might be. (Of course, solutions to $x^{5/3} = \sin(x)$ will be the x values of the intersection points of $y = x^{5/3}$ and $y = \sin(x)$.) The graph is displayed below and it is obvious that three solutions to $x^{5/3} = \sin(x)$ exist. In addition to $x = 0$, there are two other solutions and they are equally distant from 0.

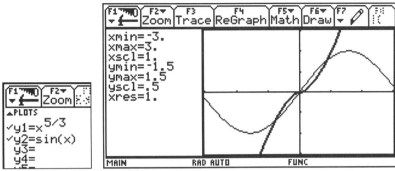

The negative solution to $x^{5/3} = \sin(x)$ is between -1 and -.5; the positive solution is between .5 and 1.

After we select the numeric equation solver application, we enter the equation, choose an upper and lower bound for a solution, and select "solve" ([F2]).

Left: Select the numeric solver from the [APPS] menu. Center: Enter the desired equation and upper and lower bounds for a numeric solution. Right: With the cursor on the "$x =$ " line, press [F2] to solve.

Constants and Measurement Units

The "units" menu is found by pressing [♦]P on the TI-92 PLUS. (On the TI-89, it is the [2nd] function of the numeric 3 key.) This menu appears below and is useful entering numbers along with their units in formulas, converting a measure from one system to another (English and SI), or even for creating your own user-defined units.

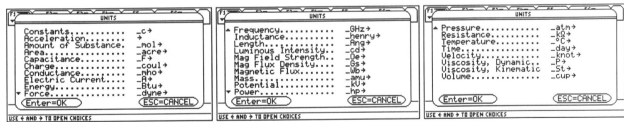

There are 28 lines to the units menu.

Notice that a unit-name is distinguished by its leading underscore character. Before we give some examples of using these units, the reader should be careful to note the system of measurement for output. That is determined in the third page of the [MODE] menu:

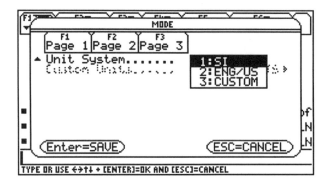

Every elementary physics student knows Newton's second law: force equals mass times acceleration, $F = m \cdot a$. To find the force that a mass of 4.5 kilograms exerts as a result of the acceleration due to gravity, we would multiply 4.5_kg times _g (the gravitational constant $\approx 9.8 \text{m/s}^2$). We show the calculation and the result, 44.1299 newtons, below:

$$\blacksquare \ \_g \qquad\qquad\qquad\qquad 9.80665 \cdot \frac{\_m}{\_s^2}$$

$$\blacksquare \ 4.5 \cdot \_kg \cdot \_g \qquad\qquad\qquad 44.1299 \cdot \_N$$

```
4.5*_kg*_g
MAIN        RAD AUTO       FUNC 2/30
```

We find that entering units is easier (if you know the precise name) from the keyboard than from the menu. The underscore character is [2nd] P on the TI-92 PLUS and [♦] [MODE] on the TI-89.

To convert from one system to another or to convert units within a system, use the conversion key, ►.[5] It is found on a TI-92 PLUS by pressing [2nd] Y and on a TI-89 by pressing [♦] [MODE]. For example, I have a 1968 Torino with a 390 in³ engine and I want to convert that to liters to compare it to some recent engines (whose displacement is usually given in the metric system). The following screen accomplishes the goal and the equivalent metric measure is about 6.39 liters:

$$\blacksquare \ 390 \cdot \_in^3 \ \blacktriangleright \ \_l \qquad\qquad\qquad 6.39095 \cdot \_l$$

```
390*_in^3▶_l
MAIN        RAD AUTO       FUNC 1/30
```

Notice that in³ is not in the menu of volume measures. We enter it by raising _in to the third power.

The CUSTOM key

Sometimes it is difficult to find a particular command or inconvenient to type it. For that reason, we can add a customized menu system for those often used or hard-to-find commands or symbols.

---

[5] The only exception to this is temperature conversion. For temperature conversion, you must use the tmpCnv(command found in the catalog. To convert 50°F to degrees Celsius, for example, you would enter the tmpCnv(50_°F,_°C):

$$\blacksquare \ tmpCnv(50 \cdot \_^\circ F, \_^\circ C) \qquad\qquad 10. \cdot \_^\circ C$$

```
tmpCnv(50_°F,_°C)
MAIN        RAD AUTO       FUNC 1/30
```

We have provided the program cust89() which will give you an idea as to how to write a program that will access the [2nd][CUSTOM] key. First, run the program by entering cust89() on the HOME screen and then observe a new menu system (displayed below).

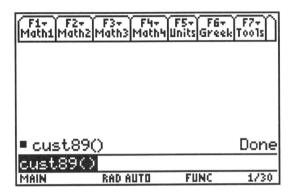

This program creates seven pull down menus labeled "Math1," "Math2," "Math3," "Math4," "Units," "Greek," and "Tools." If you press the [2nd][CUSTOM] key again, the default menu system is redisplayed.

Since the options available through CUST89() are mostly programs or functions that are explained in the explorations, we do not elaborate on them here. In the screens below, we do display the options associated with each function key.

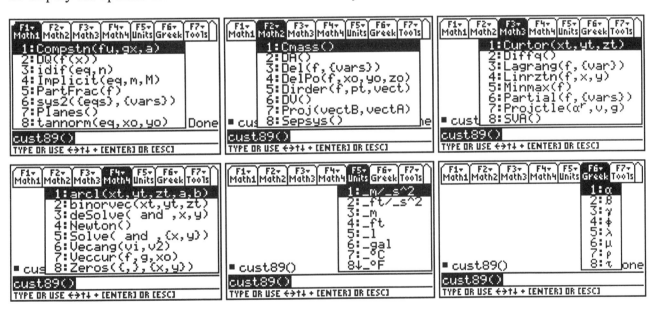

The menus above help the user regarding necessary input parameters. For example, to run the program Cmass() found in [F2], no parameters are necessary (because no variables appear within parentheses). But the to run the program for implicit differentiation, idif(eq,n) found in [F1], you will need to provide an equation (eq) as well as the order of the derivative (n).

Finally, the menu under [F7] provides a variety of handy utilities. The second option, for example, saves you from typing the word "answer" -- the variable location of most program results. This is particularly useful when a result is long and does not fit on the I/O output screen. From the home screen enter "answer" and the result can be scrolled. For all the utilities on CUST89()'s ⬚F7 menu, see the screen below:

Text Files

We conclude this *Overview* by mentioning that it is sometimes convenient to save work done on the home screen or to create a series of important definitions or other commands. This is done by saving a home screen in a text file or creating a new text file in the text editor (from the APPS key). This latter concept is sometimes referred to as **scripting.**

We have included two text files for you to peruse. They are coors.txt and minmaxt.txt.

Exploration #1
The Definition of Derivative

Example 1   Use the program defder() to find general expressions for the slope of the secant line and the slope of the tangent line for the function $f(x) = 6 - \frac{x^2}{2}$

Solution: The function $f(x) = 6 - \frac{x^2}{2}$ is entered by way of a dialog box upon program execution. [1]

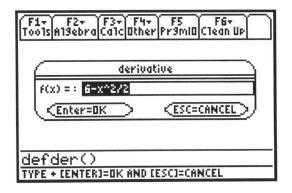

As we observe in the two screens below, the slope of the secant line is a function of both x and h and is given by $-x - \frac{h}{2}$. The slope of the tangent line is

$f'(x) = -x$

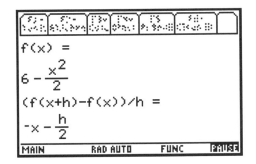 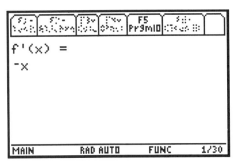

Example 2   Use the results of Example 1 to determine the equation of the secant line connecting the following two points on the graph of $y = 6 - \frac{x^2}{2}$: (-2, 4) and (1, 5.5).

---

[1] Enter defder() from the home screen.

Solution: The value of h here is the difference of the two abscissas, so $h = 3$. There-fore, the slope of the secant line is $-x - \dfrac{h}{2} = 2 - 1.5 = 0.5$. The equation of the secant line is found by using the point-slope form of a straight line $\left(y = m(x - x_1) + y_1\right)$ and is $y = 0.5(x + 2) + 4 = 0.5x + 5$. We graph the function and the secant line in the figure below.

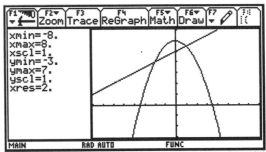

The secant line $y = 0.5x + 5$ passes through the points (-2, 4) and (1, 5.5).

Example 3   Use the results of Example 1 to determine the equation of the line drawn tangent line to the graph of $y = 6 - \dfrac{x^2}{2}$ at the point (-2, 4).

Solution: Think of the point (1, 5.5) moving toward the fixed point (-2, 4) in the fig-ure in Example 2. Equivalently, think of h approaching zero. From Example 1, the (general) expression representing slope is $f'(x) = -x$. Now, with $x = -2$, the slope of the tangent line is 2 and the point-slope form gives us: $y = 2(x + 2) + 4 = 2x + 8$. We plot that line along with the function below:

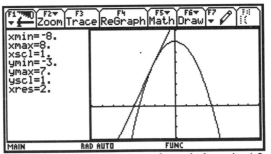

The tangent line $y = 2x + 8$ passes through the point (-2, 4).

We have seen that the general expression for the slope of the tangent line is $-x$ for the function $y = 6 - \dfrac{x^2}{2}$. So, to generalize, at any point $\left(c,\ 6 - \dfrac{c^2}{2}\right)$, the equation of the tan-gent line could be written as $y = -c(x - c) + 6 - \dfrac{c^2}{2}$. The figure below is the plot of 13 such lines (where c goes from -3 to 3 in increments of .5). The list is generated using the *seq* command:

$$\blacksquare \ \text{seq}\left(\text{-}c\cdot(x-k)+6-\frac{c^2}{2}, c, \text{-}3, 3, .5\right)$$

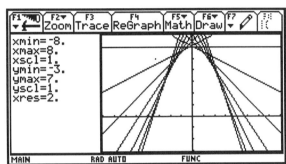

There are thirteen tangent lines drawn, each of the form

$$y=-c(x-c)+6-\frac{c^2}{2} \quad \text{at} \ x=c \ \text{when} \ c \ \text{varies from} \ -3 \ \text{to} \ 3 \ \text{in increments of .5.}$$

The figure above illustrates that the derivative characterizes the shape of a curve. After all, although only straight lines are drawn, the shape of the curve is clearly visible. It is even more pronounced with a larger number of tangent lines (but the time necessary to draw these lines increases as well).

Example 4   Use the function *tangent* provided on the accompanying diskette to determine the equation of the line drawn tangent line to the graph of

$$y = 6 - \frac{x^2}{2} \quad \text{at the point (-2, 4).}$$

Solution: The function "tangent(" takes as its parameters a function of x and a value at which the tangent line is to be evaluated. In the screen below, we see that the tangent line's equation $y = 2x - 8$ is returned.

```
■ tangent(6 - x²/2, -2)          y = 2·x + 8
tangent(6-x^2/2,-2)
MAIN        RAD AUTO        FUNC 1/30
```

$\blacksquare$

Finally, we point out that it is easy to *create* a function that will return the equation of a tangent line drawn to a curve at a particular point (x_0, y_0). Suppose we begin with a function, $f(x) = 3x^2 - x^3$ and a point (-1, 4). By defining the function tanln as follows:

define $\mathrm{tanln}\left(f, x_0, y_0\right) = \left.\dfrac{df}{dx}\right|_{x=x_0}(x - x_0) + y_0$, we can evaluate $\mathrm{tanln}\left(3x^2 - x^3, -1, 4\right)$. The screen below shows that the equation of the tangent line is $y = -9x - 5$.

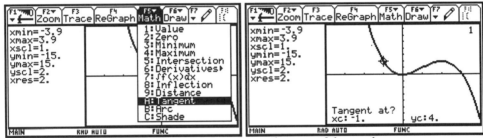

Keep in mind it is good practice to periodically clear single variable expressions (⌐F6⌐ from the HOME screen) to avoid using a variable name that has been already assigned.

Of course, there is also a "Tangent" command available from the graphics "Math" menu. Below, we have $f(x) = 3x^2 - x^3$ entered as $y1(x)$. After it is graphed, we choose "A:Tangent" from the math menu and when prompted for a point, either trace to or enter the x value of -1.

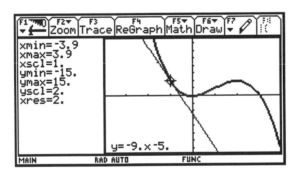

Left: Choose "A:Tangent" from the math menu of the graph screen
Right: Move the cursor to $x=-1$ or simply enter -1 from the keyboard.

Problems:

In questions 1 through 5, find the equation of the secant line connecting the points at x_1 and x_2 . Also, find the equation of the line drawn tangent to the graph of the function at x_3 .

1. $f(x) = x - x^3,\ x_1 = 0,\ x_2 = 4,\ x_3 = 2$

2. $f(x) = \dfrac{1}{x^2 - 9},\ x_1 = -2,\ x_2 = 2,\ x_3 = 1$

3. $f(x) = \dfrac{x+1}{x-1},\ x_1 = 2,\ x_2 = 4,\ x_3 = 3$

4. $f(x) = \sqrt[3]{x},\ x_1 = -8,\ x_2 = 8,\ x_3 = 2$

5. $f(x) = e^{-x^2},\ x_1 = -2,\ x_2 = 2,\ x_3 = 0$

6. What is the equation of the tangent line drawn to the graph of $f(x) = \sqrt[3]{x}$ at $(0,0)$?

7. For convenience, we have provided the function DQ(f(x)) which represents the difference quotient for the function *f(x)*. It returns the expression $\dfrac{f(x+h)-f(x)}{h}$ in x and h. To find the difference quotient for $f(x) = 3x^2 - x^3$ select DQ() from the CUST89() menu or simply type $\mathrm{DQ}\left(3x^2 - x^3\right)$ on the home screen edit line. We also evaluated the output with $x = -1$ and $h = .001$.

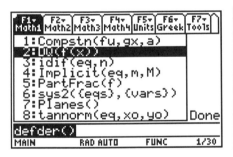

For a particular function, for example $f(x) = x - x^3$, the difference quotient represents the slope of the secant line drawn from $x = x_1$ and $x = x_1 + h$. For small values of *h*, the value of the secant line slope approaches the value of the tangent line slope (and hence, the value of the first derivative of the function at that point). Let *h* be a very small number, say 0.00001 and show that the evaluation of dq($x - x^3$) approaches the value you obtained in question 1.

8. Refer to question 7. With $f(x) = e^{-x^2}$ and $h = 0.0000001$, evaluate the difference quotient at $x_1 = 0$ and compare with your answer to question 5.

9. Use the function "tangent(" to find the equation of the tangent line drawn to the circle $x^2 + y^2 = 25$ at $x = -3$. (Hint: There are two answers and you must enter each of the two semi-circles (above and below the x-axis) separately.

Mathematical Background: If $(x, f(x))$ and $(x+h, f(x+h))$ are two points on the graph of $y = f(x)$, then the slope of the equation of the *secant line* connecting those two points is given by $\dfrac{f(x+h) - f(x)}{h}$. This expression is sometimes referred to as the *difference quotient*.

As the two points approach each other, the secant line approaches a *tangent line*. Also, as the two points approach each other, h approaches 0 (in symbols, $h \to 0$) and the slope is the first derivative of the function at the point $(x, f(x))$. More formally, we say that the definition of the first derivative of a function $y = f(x)$ is

$$f'(x) = \frac{dy}{dx} = \lim_{h \to 0} \frac{f(x+h) - f(x)}{h}.$$

Finally, we refer often to the *point-slope form of a straight line*. That is, the line passing through the point (x_1, y_1) with slope m is given by $y = m(x - x_1) + y_1$.

Program syntax: This exploration uses the program defder() which provides us with the convenience of calculating both the equation of the secant line and the equation of the tangent line. The function is entered via a dialog box. The expression representing the slope of the secant line is stored in the variable *answer* and the expression representing the slope of the tangent line is stored in the variable *answer2*.

The function dq() takes as an argument a function of x and returns the difference quotient (an expression involving x and h).

The function tangent() takes as parameters a function of x and a numerical value; it returns the equation of the tangent line drawn to the graph of the function at the value.

Exploration #2
Newton's Method

To explore Newton's method, we use the program newton() which takes no parameters and gives the user the following popup menu upon running it:

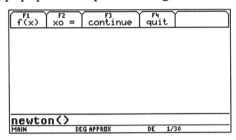

Recall that Newton's method is iterative and finds an estimate (x_{n+1}) for the zero of a function based on a previous value (x_n). The first input value is called the *guess* and here, we denote that guess by x_0. In general, we write $x_{n+1} = x_n - \dfrac{f(x_n)}{f'(x_n)}$.

Example 1   Consider the function $f(x) = x^3 + x^2 - 4x + 1$. A quick graph shows us that *f* has three real zeros. Find the largest one.

Solution: The graph of $y = x^3 + x^2 - 4x + 1$ below shows us that a good initial guess to approximate the largest zero of *f* is $x_0 = 2$.

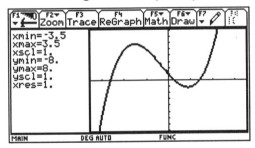

Using the program newton(), we enter the function and the initial guess and obtain the output as seen below:

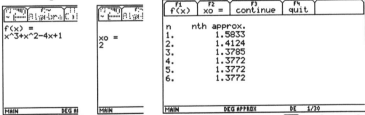

Left: Press [F1] and enter the function. Center: Press [F2] and enter 2.
Right: The first six iterations appear on the I/O screen.

Thus, we conclude that the largest zero of *f* is about 1.3772.

We point out here that an alternative to this program is to define a function $n(x)$ as below:

$$\text{Define } n(x) = x - \frac{f(x)}{\frac{d}{dx}(f(x))} \qquad \text{Done}$$

Now, to find the result of the sixth iteration with an initial guess of 2, for example, we find $n(n(n(n(n(n(2))))))$:

$$
\begin{aligned}
&\text{Define } n(x) = x - \frac{f(x)}{\frac{d}{dx}(f(x))} \qquad &\text{Done}\\
&\text{Define } f(x) = x^3 + x^2 - 4\cdot x + 1 \qquad &\text{Done}\\
&n(n(n(n(n(n(2)))))) \qquad &1.3772
\end{aligned}
$$

n(n(n(n(n(n(2))))))

MAIN   DEG AUTO   FUNC 3/30

To avoid a very lengthy fraction, we press ◆ ENTER to get the decimal approximation.

Another alternative is to view the function $n(x)$ in sequence/web mode. Select "SEQUENCE" under function from the MODE menu. Then, from the [Y=] editor, enter the iteration function as:

```
F1     F2   F3   F4   F5   F6    F7
   Zoom Edit    All Style Axes...
▲PLOTS
✓ u1=u1(n - 1) - f(x)/[d/dx(f(x))] | x = u1(n - 1)
ui1=2
```

From the [F7] "Axes" menu, select the web/trace options. After a few taps of the right cursor key, the graph converges upon the approximation 1.3772029.

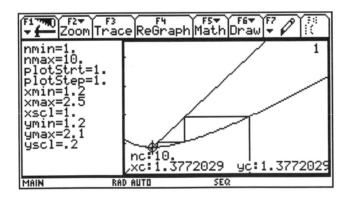

Example 2 Use Newton's method to approximate the real zeros of $f(x) = e^{-x^2} - \frac{1}{2}$ to three decimal places.

Solution: By symmetry, it suffices to find just the positive zero. It appears, from the graph below, that $x = 1$ is a good initial guess:

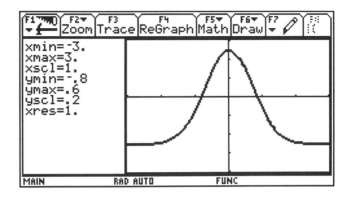

This time, we create a list of the first four iterations and see that, to three decimal places, the zero of *f* is 0.833.

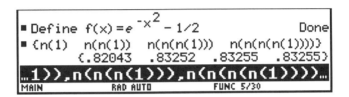

Finally, we conclude that the two zeros are $x = \pm 0.833$

Example 3   In the function from Example 1, $f(x) = x^3 + x^2 - 4x + 1$, we used an initial guess of $x = 2$ to find the desired zero. Plot the function $y = n(n(n(x)))$ to determine some **bad** initial guesses.

Solution: Notice in the graph below of $y = n(n(n(x)))$, there are three flat portions -- corresponding to the three real zeros of *f*. They occur at -2.651, 0.274, and 1.377. In two places, there are vertical asymptotes (corresponding to the two *x* values where the derivative of *f* is zero). One of those asymptotes is approximately $x \approx 0.868517$. If we use that value for our initial guess, the approximated zero is -714596!

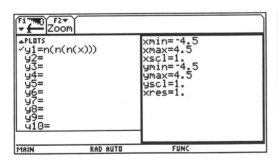
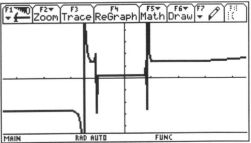

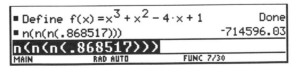

Problems:

In questions 1 through 5, use the program newton() to approximate a zero of the given function for the specified initial guess. Express the approximation after 3 and after 6 iterations by completing the table.

Function	Initial Guess	Approx. zero After 3 iterations	Approx. zero after 6 iterations
1. $f(x) = x^3 + x^2 - 4x + 1$	0		
2. $f(x) = x^3 + x^2 - 4x + 1$	-3		
3. $f(x) = x^4 - 3x^3 - 3x - 1$	-2		
4. $f(x) = x^4 - 3x^3 - 3x - 1$	6		
5. $f(x) = \cos(x^2)$	3		

6. Consider the function $f(x) = x^2 - 60$ which has as one of its zeros $\sqrt{60}$. Use six iterations of Newton's method with an appropriate initial guess to approximate $\sqrt{60}$.

7. Approximate e using six iterations of Newton's method using $f(x) = -1 + \ln x$. Use 2.5 as an initial guess.

8. Using exercise 6 as a guide, use Newton's method on a suitable function to approximate $\sqrt[3]{501}$. Use 8 as an initial guess.

9. Suppose $f(x) = \sqrt{7x-1}$. Newton's method fails here if you use an initial guess of 1. Explain. Also, try using a web plot to visualize what is happening here.

10. Consider the function $f(x) = x^4 - 4x - 6$. What happens when Newton's method is applied in the first iteration with an initial guess of $x = 1$?

11. Name two bad initial guesses for $f(x) = 30x^7 - 245x^6 + 504x^5 + 70x^3 - 735x^2 + 2520x - 20000$.

12. Newton's method is handy in cases where the command "solve(" fails. For example, there are three solutions to the equation $x^{5/3} = \sin(x)$. One of them is the trivial $x = 0$. Graph the function $f(x) = x^{5/3} - \sin(x)$ to determine a good initial guess of one of the other solutions (appearing graphically as an x intercept of f) and approximate it to four decimal places. The third solution can be found by symmetry.

Mathematical Background: Newton's method is a recursive formula and finds an estimate (x_{n+1}) for the zero of a function based on a previous value (x_n). The first input value is called the *initial guess* and here, we denote the guess by x_0. In general, we write

$x_{n+1} = x_n - \dfrac{f(x_n)}{f'(x_n)}$. If the sequence of x_n's approaches a zero of f then the process is successful in that each iteration provides an improved approximation to a zero of f.

Program syntax: The program newton() takes no parameters and allows the user to input a function and an initial guess via a pop-up menu.

NOTES

Exploration #3
Implicit Differentiation

When a function is not ***explicitly*** solved for the dependent variable (as in $y = \sqrt{9 - x^2}$, for example) we may need to differentiate ***implicitly*** (that is term-by-term, from left to right) and then solve for $\frac{dy}{dx}$. In fact, implicit differentiation allows us to find a derivative even if the relation is not a function.

Example 1   a) Find $\frac{dy}{dx}$ if $3\left(x^2 + y^2\right)^2 = 100xy$ b) Find the value of $\frac{dy}{dx}$ when $x = 1$ and $y = 3$.

Solution: a) We enter idif$\left(3\left(x^2 + y^2\right)^2 = 100 \cdot x \cdot y, 1\right)$ to determine $\frac{dy}{dx}$:

So, $\frac{dy}{dx} = \dfrac{-3x^3 - 3xy^2 + 25y}{3x^2 y - 25x + 3y^3}$

b)   The answer, of course, has been saved in ***ans(1)***. To evaluate the derivative we simply evaluate ans(1) with $x = 1$ and $y = 3$ on the home screen immediately after running idif:

We see that $\left.\dfrac{dy}{dx}\right|_{x=1, y=3} = \dfrac{9}{13}$.

44

Example 2   Find the equations for the tangent line and the normal line drawn to the curve $3(x^2 + y^2)^2 = 100xy$ at the point (1, 3).

Solution: We run tannorm($3(x^2 + y^2)^2 = 100xy$, 1, 3) and see the output below:

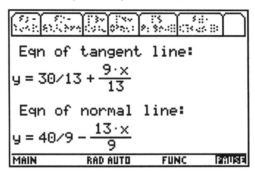

Below, we graphed the curve[2] as well as the tangent and normal lines:

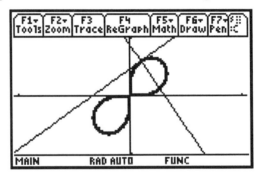

We conclude this exploration with an example of finding the second derivative implicitly.

Example 3   Find y'' for the circle $x^2 + y^2 = 100$ and discuss the curve's concavity.

Solution: The program idif($x^2 + y^2 = 100, 2$) will compute the second derivative:

---

[2] We used the program implicit() to plot the curve which is a type of curve called a ***lemniscate***. The program requires the equation as well as a minimum value for x and y. For this graph, we entered implicit$\left(3(x^2 + y^2) = 100xy, -3, 3\right)$. This can also be found under F1 in the CUST89() menu. See below:

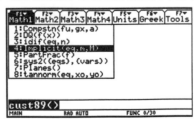

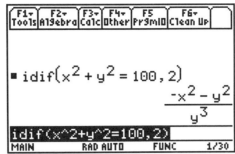

Although this result is not wrong, we prefer to write $y'' = \dfrac{-100}{y^3}$ and it is easy

to observe that the curve is concave downward if $y > 0$ and concave upward if $y < 0$ (not surprising since the curve is a circle centered at the origin!).

∎

Problems:

1. Consider the relation $2xy^2 + 3y^2 = 1$.

    a) Find $\dfrac{dy}{dx}$ by hand and then check your result using the idif() program.

    b) Determine the equation of the tangent line drawn to the point $(-1,1)$.

    c) Determine the equation of the normal line drawn to the point $(-1,1)$.

    d) Sketch the relation, the tangent line and the normal line.

2. Consider the relation $\dfrac{1}{x} + \dfrac{1}{y} = 1$.

    a) Find $\dfrac{dy}{dx}$ by hand and then check your result using the idif() program.

    b) Determine the equation of the tangent line drawn to the point $(-1, 0.5)$.

    c) Determine the equation of the normal line drawn to the point $(-1, 0.5)$.

    e) Sketch the relation, the tangent line and the normal line.

3. Consider the relation $y^2 = \dfrac{x^2-1}{x^2+1}$.

    a) Find $\dfrac{dy}{dx}$ by hand and then check your result using the idif() program.

    b) The program tannorm() fails to give correct equations for the tangent line and the normal line drawn to the point $(-1,0)$. What are the correct answers for these lines?

4.   a) Find $\dfrac{d^2y}{dx^2}$ for the ellipse $x^2 + 3y^2 = 12$.

    b) Discuss the ellipse's concavity based on your answer to part a).

Mathematical Background: When a function or relation is defined *implicitly* involving two variables, say x and y, the derivative of y with respect to x is given by $\dfrac{dy}{dx}$ and found by a process referred to as *implicit differentiation*. For example, to find $\dfrac{dy}{dx}$ given $y^2 = x$ we write $2y\dfrac{dy}{dx} = 1$ or $\dfrac{dy}{dx} = \dfrac{1}{2y}$.

In this exploration, we also examine equations of tangent lines and normal lines for curves expressed implicitly.

Program syntax: The function idif(equation,n) will return either the first order derivative $\dfrac{dy}{dx}$ (if n is 1) or the second order derivative $\dfrac{d^2y}{dx^2}$ (if n is 2). Entering idif(y^2=x,1), for example, returns $\dfrac{1}{2y}$.

A third program, tannorm(equation,x0,y0), can be used to find the equation of a tangent line or the equation of a normal line drawn to a curve at the point (x0, y0). Entering tannorm(y^2=x,4,2), for example, will find the equation of the line drawn tangent to $y^2 = x$ at (4, 2) as well as the line perpendicular to it at that point (that is, the normal line).

To plot an implicit relation, we use the utility function *implicit(*equation,xmin, ymin*)*.

Exploration #4
The Chain Rule

To understand the chain rule in calculus, it is important to get an understanding of the composition of functions. Consider $y = \sqrt{2x^3 + x - 5}$. There are two major components on the right hand side: the square root and the polynomial. Thinking of the square root function as $f(u) = \sqrt{u}$ and the polynomial as $g(x) = 2x^3 + x - 5$, we can write $y = f(g(x))$. The program (actually, it is a function) compstn(fu,gx,a) will evaluate $\dfrac{dy}{dx}$ at $x = a$. It can be typed from the edit line or is accessible from the CUST89() menu:

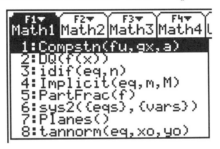

Example 1   Use compstn() to evaluate $\dfrac{dy}{dx}$ at $x = 2$ if $y = \sqrt{2x^3 + x - 5}$.

Solution: We enter $\text{compstn}\left(\sqrt{u}, 2x^3 + x - 5, 2\right)$ and find both exact and approximate forms.

```
■ compstn(√u, 2·x³ + x − 5, 2)          25·√13
                                        ────
                                         26
■ compstn(√u, 2·x³ + x − 5, 2)
                              3.46687622641
Compstn(√(u),2x^3+x−5,2)
MAIN        RAD AUTO        FUNC 2/30
```

If you want a general expression for the derivative, replace "2" with any free variable name (you cannot use x or y). Below, we use t as the general independent variable.

```
F1▼  F2▼  F3▼  F4▼  F5▼  F6▼  F7▼
Math1 Math2 Math3 Math4 Units Greek Tools
■ compstn(√u, 2·x³ + x − 5, 2)          25·√13
                                        ────
                                         26
■ compstn(√u, 2·x³ + x − 5, 2)
                              3.46687622641
■ compstn(√u, 2·x³ + x − 5, t)
                                   1 + 6·t²
                                 ──────────
                                 2·√t + 2·t³ − 5
Compstn(√(u),2x^3+x−5,t)
MAIN        RAD AUTO        FUNC 3/30
```

Problems:

1. Consider $y = \left(2x - 5x^3\right)^4$. Write y as the composition $f\left(g(x)\right)$.

    a) $f(u) = $ _____

    b) $g(x) = $ _____

    c) $\dfrac{dy}{dx} = $ _____

    d) $\dfrac{dy}{dx}\Big|_{x=-1} = $ _____

2. Consider $y = \sqrt[3]{(3x-1)^2}$. Write y as the composition $f\left(g(x)\right)$.

    a) $f(u) = $ _____

    b) $g(x) = $ _____

    c) $\dfrac{dy}{dx} = $ _____

    d) $\dfrac{dy}{dx}\Big|_{x=3} = $ _____

3. A special case of the chain rule is the ***power rule***, $\dfrac{d}{dx}\left[\left(u(x)\right)^n\right] = n\left[u(x)\right]^{n-1}\dfrac{du}{dx}$. Evaluate

$$\boxed{\texttt{d((u(x))\^n,x)}}$$

Mathematical Background: If $y = f(u)$ is a differentiable function of u and $u = g(x)$ is a differentiable function of x, then $y = f\left(g(x)\right)$ is a differentiable function of x and

$$\dfrac{dy}{dx} = \dfrac{dy}{du}\cdot\dfrac{du}{dx} \quad \text{or} \quad \dfrac{d}{dx}\left[f\left(g(x)\right)\right] = f'\left(g(x)\right)\cdot g'(x).$$

Program syntax: The function compstn(fu,gx,a) takes as its arguments, a function of u, a function of x and a value a. It returns $\dfrac{dy}{dx}\Big|_{x=a}$.

Exploration #5
Area and the Fundamental Theorem of Calculus

The area between the x axis and the continuous curve $y = f(x)$ can be approximated by drawing rectangles between curve and the axis. As the number of rectangles increases, the approximation of the area (usually) becomes better. The rectangles' lengths can be determined by the left-side length, the right-side length, the longer of the two lengths (an upper bound on the approximation), the shorter of the two lengths (a lower bound on the approximation), or the average of the two lengths (often called the *midpoint* and equivalent to approximating by drawing trapezoids under the curve).

The program arearex() provides a visualization of four of these rectangular area approximations; it also provides a table of seven different approximations to compare the different methods.

Example 1   Estimate the area under the curve $y = 9 - x^2$ and the x-axis between
$x = 0$ and $x = 3$ using 10 "right" rectangles.

Solution: We manually establish the function as $y1$ in the Y= editor and choose suitable window values before running the program.

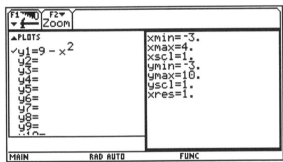

Before the program is run, we first enter the function and a suitable set of window values.

After a screen display to warn you to have your function entered, you are asked to input the left endpoint (0) and the right endpoint (3). The next step is to choose F5 so that we can enter our value of n, 10.

The program creates a toolbar with seven options.

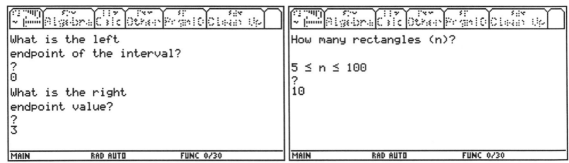

Left: The program prompts for endpoint values.
Right: Select F5 to change the number of rectangles from the default of 20 to the desired value of 10

We see that the area using 10 right rectangles is about 16.605 square units.

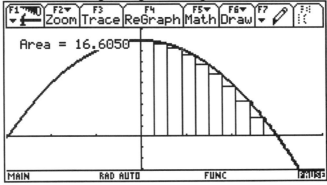

Option F6 creates a table for comparing a variety of approximations:

```
With 10 Rectangles
Left      19.3050
Right     16.6050
Upper     19.3050
Lower     16.6050
Midpt     17.9550
Integral 18.0000
```

Example 2   Using eight rectangles, compare the "left", "right", "lower", and "upper" approximations for the area under the curve $y = -x^3 - x^2 + 4x + 4$ and the x-axis between $x = -1$ and $x = 2$. Between what two values can you be assured the actual area is?

Solution: The four approximations are shown below:

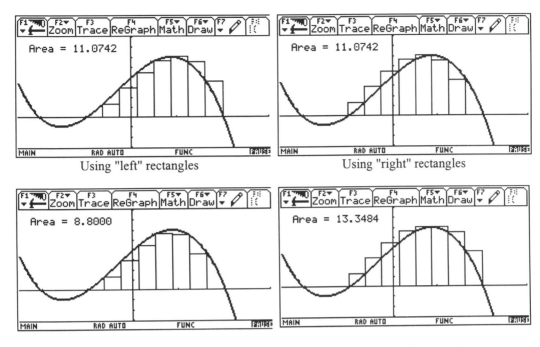

Using "left" rectangles   Using "right" rectangles

Using "lower" rectangles   Using "upper" rectangles

We know the actual area must be between 8.8 and 13.3484 square units. We provide the table of approximations using 100 rectangles for the sake of comparison.

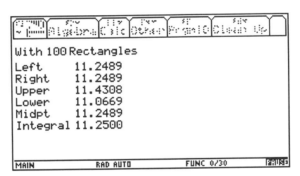

We conclude this exploration by pointing out that there is a built-in "area-finder" and it can be found after graphing a function in the "Math" menu. We stress here, however, the importance of understanding the notion of a sum (of areas, in this case) representing a definite integral. As the number of terms in that sum increases, the closer we come to representing the definite integral. A screen capture for the area of Example 2 appears below:

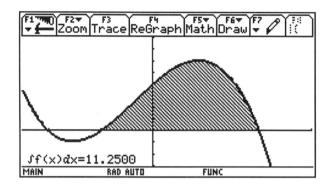

Problems:

1. Approximate the area between $f(x) = x^2$ on $0 \le x \le 4$ using:
   b) Four "left" rectangles.
   c) Four "right" rectangles.
   d) Using 20 "upper" and 20 "lower" rectangle approximations, between what two numbers can you be assured $\int_0^4 x^2 \, dx$ is?

2. Approximate the area between $f(x) = \sqrt{x}$ on $1 \le x \le 4$ using:
   b) 40 "left" rectangles.
   c) 40 "right" rectangles.
   d) Using 20 "upper" and 20 "lower" rectangle approximations, between what two numbers can you be assured $\int_1^4 \sqrt{x} \, dx$ is?

3. Approximate $\int_0^\pi x \sin(x) \, dx$ using $n = 8$ rectangles. Use both "lower" and "upper" approximations.

4. Approximate $\int_1^2 \frac{1}{x^2} \, dx$ using $n = 20$ rectangles. Use both "lower" and "upper" approximations.

5. If a function has no closed form antiderivative, then approximation is about the only way we can evaluate a definite integral. Estimate the value of $\int_0^1 \sin(x^2) \, dx$ using the program arearex(). Use 50 rectangles.

6. Repeat exercise 5 for $\int_0^{\sqrt{\pi}} \sin(x^2) \, dx$.

7. In the study of statistics, the function $f(x) = \dfrac{1}{\sqrt{2\pi}} e^{-x^2/2}$ is called *the standard normal*

probability density function and tables of values to compute $\displaystyle\int_0^z \dfrac{1}{\sqrt{2\pi}} e^{-x^2/2} dx$ are an essen-

tial part of every book on statistics.

a) Approximate $\displaystyle\int_0^1 \dfrac{1}{\sqrt{2\pi}} e^{-x^2/2} dx$ using the arearex() program with $n = 10$ "upper" rec-

tangles.

b) From a table of values, we found that to four decimal place precision, the value of

$\displaystyle\int_0^1 \dfrac{1}{\sqrt{2\pi}} e^{-x^2/2} dx$ is approximately .3413. How many "upper" rectangles are necessary

to match that precision?

Mathematical Background: The *Fundamental Theorem of Integral Calculus* states that if
f is a continuous function on the interval $a \le x \le b$ and if F is an antiderivative of f,

then $\displaystyle\int_a^b f(x)\, dx = F(x)\Big]_a^b = F(b) - F(a)$. Furthermore, if the function f is positive in

that interval, then this value also represents the area between the curve and the x-axis
over that interval.

We can approximate this (continuous) area with a discrete number of geometric objects -- in the case of this exploration, rectangles. Other objects could be used and in fact trapezoids are often studied in this light as are parabolic arcs (using Simpson's Rule). As the number of these rectangles increases, so does the approximation of the rectangles' area to the actual area.

Program Syntax: The arearex() program requires no arguments. The program creates a toolbar menu which is self explanatory. It is important to remember, though, that the desired function must be entered as $y1$ ***prior*** to running the program. Also, before running the program choose suitable graphing window values.

NOTES

Exploration #6
Simpson's Rule

Example 1   Estimate $\int_{-2}^{2}\left(-x^6 + 20x^2 + 10x + 40\right)dx$ using Simpson's Rule first with

$n = 4$ and then with $n = 8$ subdivisions.

Solution: We manually assign $-x^6 + 20x^2 + 10x + 40$ to $y1(x)$ in the Y= editor and
then enter simpson1(-2,2,4) from the home screen. The syntax for this program is simpson1(a,b,n) where a is the lower bound, b is the upper bound, and
n is the number of subdivisions.

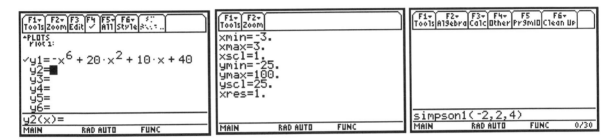

Setup for simpson1. Step 1: Enter the function in the Y= editor. Step 2: Enter suitable WINDOW values.
Step 3: From the HOME screen, enter simpson1(a,b,n)

We obtain the following output:

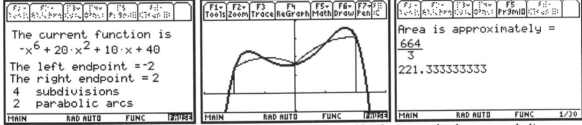

With $n = 4$ subdivisions, the area under the function is approximated by the area under the two parabolic arcs.

$$\int_{-2}^{2}\left(-x^6 + 20x^2 + 10x + 40\right)dx \approx 221.3 \text{ sq units.}$$

Next, we use $n = 8$ subdivisions. Notice in the output below that the four
parabolic arcs are almost indistinguishable from the curve. That is, as n in-
creased, so did the accuracy of the approximation.

56

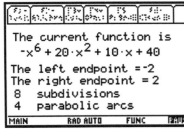 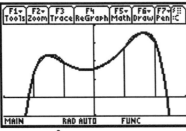 

With $n = 8$ subdivisions. $\int_{-2}^{2}\left(-x^6 + 20x^2 + 10x + 40\right)dx \approx 229.458$ sq units.

Of course, for this function we can find the *exact* value of $\int_{-2}^{2}\left(-x^6 + 20x^2 + 10x + 40\right)dx$ and we leave it to the reader to determine that value. The real advantage of Simpson's Rule is to approximate definite integrals for functions that do not have a closed form antiderivative. See the exercises and Example 3 for illustrations involving those types of integrals. ■

Example 2   How many subdivisions are necessary to insure that the Simpson Rule approximation to $\int_{-2}^{2}\left(-x^6 + 20x^2 + 10x + 40\right)dx$ is within 0.05 square units of the actual value?

Solution: We will invoke simperr(err,a,b). This program returns a value of n that insures the approximation to be less than or equal to *err*.

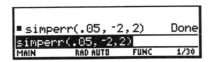

Interpretation: n must be rounded up to an *even* integer so, to insure the approximation is within 0.05 of the actual value, 22 subdivisions must be used. ■

Example 3   Approximate $\int_{0}^{1}e^{-x^2}dx$ to be within .0001 of its actual value.

Solution: We first run simperr(.0001, 0, 1) and see that subdivisions are necessary:

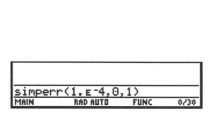 

Next, we run simpson1 and conclude that $0.7467 \le \int_0^1 e^{-x^2} dx \le 0.7469$.

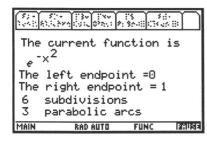 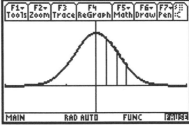 

■

Problems:

1. Find the exact value of $\int_{-2}^{2} \left(-x^6 + 20x^2 + 10x + 40\right)dx$ and compare that value with the approximations found in Example 1.

2. Approximate $\int_1^2 \sqrt{x^3 - 1}\,dx$ using $n = 4$.

3. Approximate $\int_1^2 \sqrt{x^3 - 1}\,dx$ using $n = 8$.

4. A student used this program to evaluate $\int_{-2.5}^{1} \frac{1}{x^2}\,dx$ and got 20.5187 as an approximation using $n = 6$ subdivisions. Comment on the absurdity of that result.

5. Since Simpson's Rule relies on approximating area with parabolic arcs, it should not be surprising that for quadratic functions, there is no error in Simpson's Rule. What happens if the function is linear, say $y = 2x + 3$?

6. Show that Simpson's Rule yields the *exact* area if the function is a cubic polynomial. Follow these steps as a guide:

    a) Notice the expression $M = \max\left(\left|f^{(4)}(x)\right|\right)$ on the interval $a \le x \le b$ is zero if f is the cubic polynomial $f(x) = -x^3 + 5x + 2$.

    b) Plot the function $f(x) = -x^3 + 5x + 2$ on the interval $[0, 2]$ along with three parabolic arcs ($n = 6$).

58

7. In the study of statistics, the function $f(x) = \dfrac{1}{\sqrt{2\pi}} e^{-x^2/2}$ is called *the standard normal*

probability density function and tables of values to compute $\displaystyle\int_0^z \dfrac{1}{\sqrt{2\pi}} e^{-x^2/2}\,dx$ are an essen-

tial part of every book on statistics.

a) Suppose $z = 1.5$. How many subdivisions would be necessary using Simpson's Rule to create a table entry that is accurate within 0.0001?

b) Find $\displaystyle\int_0^{1.5} \dfrac{1}{\sqrt{2\pi}} e^{-x^2/2}\,dx$ using the number of subdivisions found in part a).

Mathematical Background: 1. For this exploration, we will assume that $y = f(x)$ is a positive, continuous function in some interval $a \le x \le b$ and that n is an even number. Then the area between $y = f(x)$ and the x-axis between a and b is approximated by

$$\int_a^b f(x)\,dx \approx \frac{h}{3}\left[f(x_0) + 4f(x_1) + 2f(x_2) + 4f(x_3) + \cdots + 2f(x_{n-2}) + 4f(x_{n-1}) + f(x_n)\right]$$

where $h = \dfrac{b-a}{n}$ is the width of each subinterval. This approximation to $\displaystyle\int_a^b f(x)\,dx$ is

known as **Simpson's Rule** (or the Parabolic Rule).

Simpson's Rule uses the fact that any three non-collinear points determine a unique parabola that passes through them. We can partition the interval $a \le x \le b$ using groups of three adjacent points on the graph of $y = f(x)$ and approximating

$\displaystyle\int_a^b f(x)\,dx$ by the area under the parabolic segments. Note that since we need three

adjacent points, our partition must have an even number of subintervals.

2. The error, S_{err}, in this approximation is given by $0 \le S_{err} \le \dfrac{(b-a)^5 M}{180 n^4}$ where M is

the maximum value for $\left| f^{(4)}(x) \right|$ on the interval $a \le x \le b$.

Program Syntax: The simpson1(a,b,n) program requires three arguments: the lower bound a, the upper bound b, and the number of subdivisions, n. This program will graph the

function (which must be stored in $y1(x)$) and the $\dfrac{n}{2}$ parabolic arcs. It calls a second

program, simpson2 that then calculates the area using the formula above.
Finally, the program simperr(err,a,b) will calculate the number of subdivisions (n) necessary for an accuracy less than or equal to *err*.

Exploration #7
Taylor Polynomial Approximations

The TI-89, TI-92 and TI-92PLUS come equipped with a calculus menu item called ***Taylor***. It is used to find the Taylor polynomial of degree *n* about point *c = 0* of a given function.

Example 1   Find the fourth degree Taylor polynomial approximation to $f(x) = e^x$ about the point $x = 0$.[3]

Solution: We enter taylor(e^x,x,4,0) and the fourth degree polynomial approximation is displayed on the home screen. Below, that result as well as the graphical view of the approximation are given:

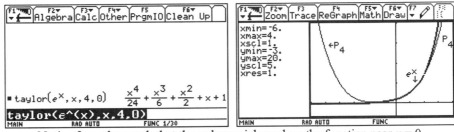

Notice from the graph that the polynomial overlaps the function near $x = 0$.

$$P_4(x) = \frac{x^4}{24} + \frac{x^3}{6} + \frac{x^2}{2} + x + 1$$

For contrast, the ninth degree polynomial is graphed along with $f(x) = e^x$ on the screen below:

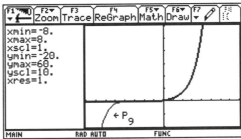

---

[3] The special case Taylor polynomial about the value $x = 0$ is often referred to as a Maclaurin polynomial.

60

In the exercises, you will see that $f(x) = e^x$ has an infinite radius of convergence; that is, as the degree of the Taylor polynomial approximation increases, the approximation is valid for a wider and wider interval.

Example 2   Find the sixth degree Taylor polynomial approximation to $f(x) = \ln x$ about the point $x = 1$.

Solution: $P_6 = -\dfrac{(x-1)^6}{6} + \dfrac{(x-1)^5}{5} - \dfrac{(x-1)^4}{4} + \dfrac{(x-1)^3}{3} - \dfrac{(x-1)^2}{2} + (x-1) = \displaystyle\sum_{k=1}^{6} (-1)^{k+1} \dfrac{(x-1)^k}{k}$

The graphs of $f(x) = \ln x$ and the sixth degree polynomial appear below:

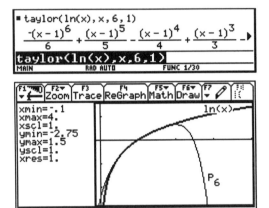

The function is graphed in "thick" style and the approximation is drawn in "line" style.

In the exercises, we see that the function $f(x) = \ln x$ has a (finite) radius of convergence equal to 1. That is, now matter how high the degree of the Taylor polynomial approximation, the region for which the approximation is valid will not increase.

Problems:

1.   a) Determine the twelfth degree Taylor polynomial approximation to $y = e^x$ at $x = 0$
b) Graph $y = e^x$ along with your answer to part a).

c) The Taylor series can be written as $\displaystyle\sum_{k=0}^{\infty} \dfrac{x^k}{k!}$. Show that $R = \displaystyle\lim_{k \to \infty} \left| \dfrac{a_k}{a_{k+1}} \right| = \infty$ where

$a_k = \dfrac{1}{k!}$. Thus, the interval of convergence is all real numbers.

2.   a) Determine the twelfth degree Taylor polynomial approximation to $y = \ln x$ at $x = 1$
b) Graph $y = \ln x$ along with your answer to part a).

c) The Taylor series can be written as $\displaystyle\sum_{k=0}^{\infty}(-1)^{k+1}\frac{(x-1)^k}{k}$. Show that

$$R=\lim_{k\to\infty}\left|\frac{a_k}{a_{k+1}}\right|=1 \text{ where } a_k=\frac{1}{k}.$$

d) The result of part c) leads us to believe that the interval of convergence is $c-R<x<c+R$ or $0<x<2$. We must check the endpoints of this interval. Since the function is not even defined at , we need check only $x=2$ for convergence in $\displaystyle\sum_{k=0}^{\infty}(-1)^{k+1}\frac{(x-1)^k}{k}$. Do that and show that the interval of convergence for $y=\ln x$ is $0<x\le2$.

In questions 3 through 8, find a) P_1, b) P_2, c) P_3, d) P_4, and e) the interval of convergence for the given function and center.

3. $y=\sin x$ about $c=0$

4. $y=\sin x$ about $c=\dfrac{\pi}{2}$

5. $y=\dfrac{1}{x}$ about $c=1$

6. $y=e^{-x}$ about $c=0$

7. $y=\tan x$ about $c=0$

8. $y=\dfrac{2}{(x+1)^2}$ about $c=0$

9. **Euler's Formula**. Use the results of this section to show:

$$e^{ix}=\sum_{k=0}^{\infty}\frac{(ix)^k}{k!}=1+ix+\frac{(ix)^2}{2!}+\frac{(ix)^3}{3!}+\dots$$

$$=\underbrace{1-\frac{x^2}{2!}+\frac{x^4}{4!}-\frac{x^6}{6!}+\dots}_{\cos x}+i\underbrace{\left(x-\frac{x^3}{3!}+\frac{x^5}{5!}-\dots\right)}_{\sin x}$$

and finally $e^{ix}=\cos x+i\sin x$.

Mathematical Background: A function f can be approximated by an nth degree Taylor polynomial, $P_n(x)$, at $x=c$ as:

$$f(x)\approx P_n(x)=f(c)+f'(c)(x-c)+f''(c)\frac{(x-c)^2}{2!}+\dots+f^{(n)}(c)\frac{(x-c)^n}{n!}$$

provided f and its first n derivatives exist at c. From Taylor's theorem, the difference between the function and its approximation (called a *remainder*) is given by

$$R_n(x) = f^{(n)}(d)\frac{(x-c)^{(n+1)}}{(n+1)!}$$, sometimes called the ***Lagrange form*** of the remainder.

Here, d is a number between x and c.

In general, a series of the form

$$\sum_{k=0}^{\infty} a_k (x-c)^k = a_0 + a_1(x-c) + \ldots + a_k(x-c)^k + \ldots$$ is called a ***power series centered***

at c. A ***Taylor series*** is a special power series form with each $a_k = \dfrac{f^{(k)}}{k!}$.

The values of x for which a series converges is called its ***interval of convergence*** and for our purposes in this exploration, can be found by examining

$$R = \lim_{k\to\infty}\left|\frac{a_k}{a_{k+1}}\right|$$. R is called the ***radius of convergence*** and determines the interval of convergence. If R is infinite then the interval of convergence is all real numbers.

Program Syntax: There is no program for this exploration. However, we use the Taylor command from the Calculus menu: *taylor(f(x),x,n,c)*.

Exploration #8
Partial Derivatives, Multiple Integrals, and Centers of Mass

Example 1. First Partial Derivatives. Suppose $f(x,y) = 5x^2 y^3 - x\sin(y)$. Find $\dfrac{\partial f}{\partial x}$ and $\dfrac{\partial f}{\partial y}$.

Solution: We could perform this directly from the keyboard as can be seen in the screen below.

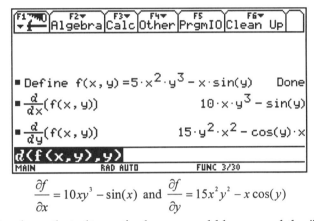

$$\frac{\partial f}{\partial x} = 10xy^3 - \sin(x) \text{ and } \frac{\partial f}{\partial y} = 15x^2 y^2 - x\cos(y)$$

We mention here that alternatively, we could have used the "partial" command (option 6 from the ⬚ Math3 menu of the CUST89() program) as we do in the next example.

∎

Example 2. Second Partials. With $f(x,y) = 5x^2 y^3 - x\sin(y)$ from Example 1, find the four second partials, $\dfrac{\partial^2 f}{\partial x^2}, \dfrac{\partial^2 f}{\partial y^2}, \dfrac{\partial^2 f}{\partial y\partial x}$, and $\dfrac{\partial^2 f}{\partial x\partial y}$.

Solution: We choose option 6 from the ⬚ Math3 menu of the CUST89() program and note the syntax: the arguments for "partial" consist of the function and a list of the independent variables in the order needed:

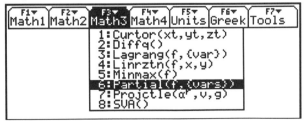

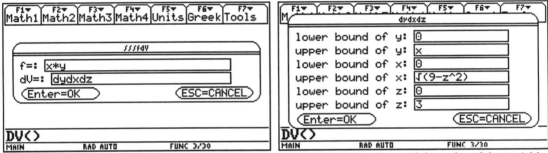

We see that $\dfrac{\partial^2 f}{\partial x^2} = 10y^3, \dfrac{\partial^2 f}{\partial y^2} = x\sin(y) + 30x^2 y,$ and $\dfrac{\partial^2 f}{\partial y \partial x} = \dfrac{\partial^2 f}{\partial x \partial y} = 30xy^2 - \cos(y)$.

■

Example 3. Multiple Integration. Evaluate $\displaystyle\int_0^3 \int_0^{\sqrt{9-z^2}} \int_0^x xy\, dy\, dx\, dz$.

Solution: While we could do this by nesting integrals, we choose "DV()" (option #6 under the [F2] Math2 menu of the CUST89() program).[1]

Left: Upon running "DV()", a dialog box appears prompting for the function and the order of the variables. Right: A second dialog box prompts for the variables' bounds. Below: The result.

■

---

[1] For double integrals, choose option #2, DA().

Example 4. Triple Integrals as Volume. Find the volume of the solid that is
bounded above by the sphere $x^2 + y^2 + z^2 = 4$ and below by the plane
$y + z = 2$.

Solution: z is bounded below by $z = 2 - y$ and above by the (upper) hemisphere
$z = \sqrt{4 - x^2 - y^2}$. The limits for x and y are determined by the projection of
the solid on the xy-plane. Setting $\sqrt{4 - x^2 - y^2}$ equal to $2 - y$ yields:

$$\sqrt{4 - x^2 - y^2} = 2 - y$$

$$x = \pm\sqrt{4y - 2y^2}$$

We see y varies between 0 and 2 and the following iterated integral evolves:

$$\int_0^2 \int_{-\sqrt{4y-y^2}}^{\sqrt{4y-y^2}} \int_{2-y}^{\sqrt{4-x^2-y^2}} dz\, dx\, dy$$

Running DV() yields the result of about 1.946 cubic units.

Example 5. Center of Mass. Use Cmass() to find the center of mass of a triangular
lamina having density function $\delta(x, y) = xy$ with vertices (0,0), (1,0), and
(0,2) as shown.

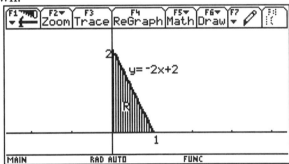

Solution: Since this is a two-dimensional problem, we select [F1] from the program's
menu. The program Cmass will display the center of mass after performing
the calculation of total mass ($\iint_R \delta(x, y)\, DA$) and the moments in the x and y
directions.

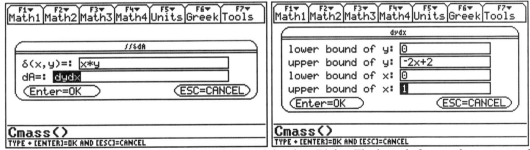

Left: We enter the density function and the differential order. Right: The bounds for x and y are entered.

The center of mass is $\left(\dfrac{2}{5}, \dfrac{4}{5}\right)$ and is output in the screen below:

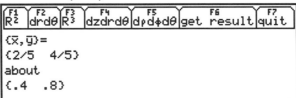

The program Cmass() can also compute the center of mass in a three dimensional co-ordinate system (the F3 menu for rectangular coordinates, F4 for cylindrical coordinates, and F5 for spherical coordinates).

Example 6. Finding the Centroid using Cylindrical Coordinates. Find the centroid of the solid bounded by the hemisphere $z = \sqrt{25 - x^2 - y^2}$, the cylinder $x^2 + y^2 = 9$, and the xy-plane.

Solution: We assume a uniform density; that is, $\delta(z, r, \theta) = 1$. After choosing option F4 from the Cmass() menu, we enter the following triple integral:

$$\int_0^{2\pi} \int_0^3 \int_0^{\sqrt{25-r^2}} 1 \, dz \, dr \, d\theta.$$ The input and output are displayed below:

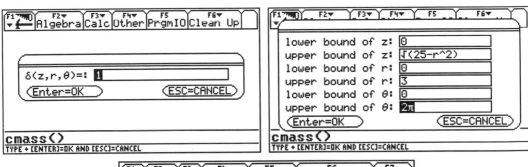

Problems:

In problems 1 through 4, find $\dfrac{\partial f}{\partial x}$, $\dfrac{\partial f}{\partial y}$, $\dfrac{\partial^2 f}{\partial x^2}$, $\dfrac{\partial^2 f}{\partial y^2}$, $\dfrac{\partial^2 f}{\partial y \partial x}$, and $\dfrac{\partial^2 f}{\partial x \partial y}$ for the given function.

1. $f(x,y) = 4x^2 y^3$

2. $f(x,y) = 4x^2 y^3 - \ln(1 - xy)$

3. $f(x,y) = y^3 \tan^{-1}\left(\dfrac{x}{y}\right)$

4. $f(x,y) = \dfrac{x-y}{1+x^2} + \sin(x^2 y)$

5. The **total differential of a function f** is defined as $\dfrac{\partial f}{\partial x}dx + \dfrac{\partial f}{\partial y}dy$. Suppose f is a function

   of x and y that is equal to 0. Show that the **implicit derivative** (studied in Calculus I) is

   none other than $y' = -\dfrac{\frac{\partial f}{\partial x}}{\frac{\partial f}{\partial y}}$.

In problems 6 through 9, evaluate each multiple integral.

6. $\displaystyle\int_0^1 \int_0^{\sqrt{1-z^2}} \int_0^x xy\, dy\, dx\, dz$

7. $\displaystyle\int_0^1 \int_0^{1+x} (3x + 2y)\, dy\, dx$

8. $\displaystyle\int_0^1 \int_0^x \sqrt{x^2 + y^2}\, dy\, dx$

9. $\displaystyle\int_0^2 \int_0^{\sqrt{4-x^2}} \int_0^{\sqrt{4-x^2-y^2}} xyz\, dz\, dy\, dx$

10. Find the volume of the solid whose base is the region in the xy plane bounded by the curve $y = 4 - x^2$ and the x and y axes, and whose top is the plane $z = 10$.

11. Find the volume of the solid whose base is the region in the xy plane bounded by the three lines $x + y = 1$, the x axis, and the y axis if the region is bounded on the top by the plane $z = 5 + x + 2y$.

12. Find the center of mass of a lamina with density $\delta(x,y) = x + 2y$ that is bounded by the x-axis, the line $x = 1$, and the curve $y = \dfrac{\sqrt{x}}{2}$.

13. A solid of uniform density is bounded below by the cone $z = \sqrt{x^2 + y^2}$ and above by the sphere $x^2 + y^2 + z^2 = 9$. Use spherical coordinates to find the center of mass of the region.

Mathematical Background: If $z = f(x,y)$ is a function of two variables, x and y then the first partial derivative of f with respect to x is found by considering y as constant. There are several ways to represent this symbolically including:

$$\frac{\partial}{\partial x} f(x,y) = \frac{\partial z}{\partial x} = f_x(x,y) = z_x = f_x.$$

The second partial derivative of $z = f(x,y)$ with respect to x both times is written:

$$\frac{\partial^2}{\partial x^2} f(x,y) = \frac{\partial^2 z}{\partial x^2} = f_{xx}(x,y) = z_{xx} = f_{xx}.$$

The second partial derivative of $z = f(x,y)$ with respect to x, then y is written:

$$\frac{\partial^2}{\partial y \partial x} f(x,y) = \frac{\partial^2 z}{\partial y \partial x} = f_{xy}(x,y) = z_{xy} = f_{xy}$$

To evaluate a multiple integral, such as $\int_0^1 \int_0^3 6x^2 y^3 \, dx\, dy$, we first integrate with respect to x (the innermost integral) holding y as a constant and then we integrate that result with respect to y:

$$\int_0^1 \left(\int_0^3 6x^2 y^3 \, dx \right) dy = \int_0^1 \left[2x^3 y^3 \right]_0^3 dy = \int_0^1 54 y^3 \, dy = 13.5.$$

If f is a continuous and nonnegative function over some region R in the xy plane, then the volume of the solid bounded on top by the surface $z = f(x,y)$ and on the bottom by the region R is given by the double integral $\iint_R f(x,y)\, dA$ where $dA = dx\, dy$ or $dA = dy\, dx$.

In two dimensions, the center of gravity (denoted $(\bar{x}, \bar{y})$) of a lamina with density $\delta(x,y)$ is given by:

$$\bar{x} = \frac{M_y}{M} = \frac{\text{moment about } y \text{ axis}}{\text{total mass of lamina}} = \frac{\iint_R x\, \delta(x,y)\, dA}{\iint_R \delta(x,y)\, dA} \quad \text{and} \quad \bar{y} = \frac{M_x}{M} = \frac{\text{moment about } x \text{ axis}}{\text{total mass of lamina}} = \frac{\iint_R y\, \delta(x,y)\, dA}{\iint_R \delta(x,y)\, dA}$$

There are obvious generalizations to three dimensions.

Program Syntax: DA() is a program for evaluating double integrals and DV() is a program for evaluating triple integrals. The program Cmass() is a program for finding the center of mass in either 2-space or 3-space and in a variety of coordinate systems (rectangular, polar, cylindrical, or spherical). Partial(f,{vars}) is a function to determine the partial derivatives. We recommend accessing all of these from the CUST89() custom menu. "Partial" is found as the sixth option in the F3 Math3 menu; DA(), DV(), and Cmass() are found in the F2 Math2 menu.

Extrema of Functions of Several Variables

Example 1. Use the program minmax() to locate all local maxima, local minima, and saddle points for the function $f(x, y) = x^2 - 2xy - 8x + 3y^2$.

Solution: Minmax(f) is option 5 under ⬚ Math3 of the CUST89() custom menu

system. We enter 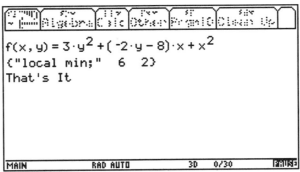 from the HOME screen and

the results are output on the I/O screen below:

A local minimum occurs when $x = 6$ and $y = 2$.

The minimum value of the function is $f(6, 2) = -24$.

A visual inspection (be sure "3D" is chosen as the graph mode) can be done also. Using the TRACE option, we see the minimum in the graph screen below:

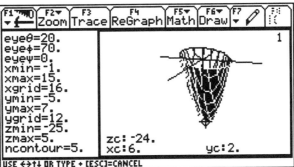

Example 2. Use the program minmax() to locate all local maxima, local minima, and saddle points for the function $f(x, y) = 8xy - 16x^4 - y^4$.

Solution: There are two local maxima occurring at $\left(\dfrac{1}{2}, 1, 2\right)$ and $\left(-\dfrac{1}{2}, -1, 2\right)$.

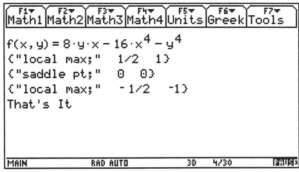

The 3D graphs below help visualize the output of the program:

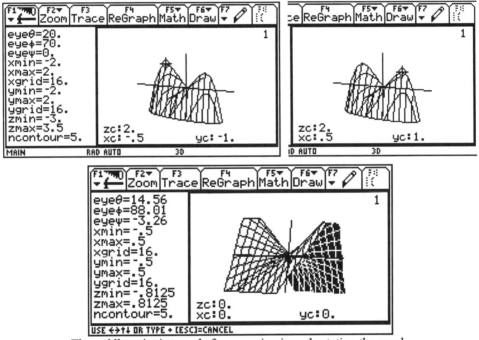

The saddle point is traced after zooming in and rotating the graph.

Problems:

In problems 1 through 8, use the program minmax() to locate all local maxima, local minima, and saddle points for the given function. Also, view the 3D graph to substantiate your answers visually.

1. $f(x,y) = 3x^2 + y^3 - 6xy - 9y + 2$

2. $f(x,y) = 3y^2 + x^3 - 6xy - 9x + 2$

3. $f(x,y) = x^2 + y^2 - 12x + 6y - 7$

4. $f(x,y) = 3x^2 + 3y^2 - 2xy - 12x + 4y - 10$

5. $f(x,y) = xy - x^2 - y^3$

6. $f(x,y) = e^{-x^2 - 2y^2}$

7. $f(x,y) = 2xy - 4y^2 - x^3$

8. $f(x,y) = x^3 + y^3 - 2x - 2y$

9. Included on the diskette of programs accompanying this manual is a text file called minmaxt.txt. Read that text file and then execute the commands in it to examine the function $f(x,y) = \dfrac{x+y}{(x^2+1)(y^2+1)}$

Mathematical Background: A *value* (a, b) is a critical value of the function $z = f(x,y)$ if $\dfrac{\partial}{\partial x} f(a,b) = f_x(a,b) = 0$ *and* $\dfrac{\partial}{\partial y} f(a,b) = f_y(a,b) = 0$. The associated triple, $(a,b,f(a,b))$ is called a *critical point* on the graph of the function.

The *second partial derivative test* states that if we calculate a number K as follows: $K = f_{xx}(a,b) \cdot f_{yy}(a,b) - \left[f_{xy}(a,b) \right]^2$ then the function f has:

a local minimum at $(a,b,f(a,b))$ if $K > 0$ and $f_{xx}(a,b) > 0$

a local maximum at $(a,b,f(a,b))$ if $K > 0$ and $f_{xx}(a,b) < 0$

a saddle point at $(a,b,f(a,b))$ if $K < 0$.

If $K = 0$ the test fails.

Program Syntax: The program minmax(f) is found as option 5 under ▣ Math3 of the CUST89() custom menu. The input parameter *f* must be a function of the two independent variables, x and y.

NOTES

Using deSolve for First Order Differential Equations

The TI-89 and TI-92 Plus come equipped with a command called *deSolve()*. Many first order differential equations (but not all!) can be solved using this command.

Example 1   Find the general solution: $\dfrac{dy}{dx} = 2x - y$.

Solution: This is a first order linear (in *y*) differential equation. The syntax for invoking deSolve() to find the general solution is shown below. In general, the parameters are the differential equation followed by the independent variable and then the dependent variable.

$$\boxed{\texttt{deSolve(y'=2*x-y,x,y)}}$$

The solution is displayed below:

$$\boxed{\begin{array}{l} \blacksquare \ \texttt{deSolve(y'} = 2 \cdot x - y, x, y) \\ \qquad\qquad y = @2 \cdot e^{-x} + 2 \cdot (x - 1) \\ \hline \texttt{deSolve(y'=2*x-y,x,y)} \\ \hline \texttt{MAIN} \qquad \texttt{RAD AUTO} \qquad \texttt{FUNC} \qquad \texttt{1/30} \end{array}}$$

The "@2" symbol stands for an arbitrary constant and may be different on your screen. We choose to write the solution as $y = c \cdot e^{-x} + 2(x - 1)$ ■

The solution $y = c \cdot e^{-x} + 2(x - 1)$ above is referred to as a ***general*** solution because of the presence of the arbitrary constant *c*. In fact, graphically the solution is actually a family of curves. Given an initial value, say that $y(0) = 3$ (or, when *x* is 0, *y* is 3) one curve in particular, $y = 5e^{-x} + 2(x - 1)$ represents the solution. This can be seen graphically by setting the graph mode to "DIFF EQUATIONS" and entering the differential equation (with *y* as a function of *t*) in the Y= editor. See the screens below and notice that as *t* increases without bound, the curve approaches the straight line $y = 2(t - 1)$.

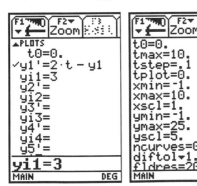
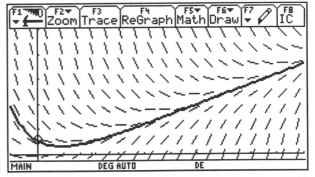

Y= Editor   WINDOW Editor   A numerically calculated graphical solution showing slope field lines.

Example 2   Find the solution to the initial value problem:
$$(4x + t - 7)dt + (8x^2 + 4t)dx = 0 \text{ with } x(-1) = 0.$$

Solution: We rewrite the differential equation (whose dependent variable is x and whose independent variable is t) in the following way:
$$(4x + t - 7) + (8x^2 + 4t)\frac{dx}{dt} = 0$$

The initial condition is entered after the differential equation and the word "and" as follows:
$$\text{deSolve}((4x + t - 7) + (8x^2 + 4t) * x' \text{ and } x(-1) = 0, t, x)$$

Notice the curiously unsimplified form of the answer (with a "-4x" on both sides). We would ordinarily express this answer as $4xt + \dfrac{t^2}{2} - 7t + \dfrac{8x^3}{3} = \dfrac{15}{2}$

Problems:

1. The differential equation of example 1, $\dfrac{dy}{dx} = 2x - y$, is a linear first-order differential equation. It can be rewritten as $\dfrac{dy}{dx} + y = 2x$ and solved by multiplying both sides of the equation by the **integrating factor** $e^{\int P(x)dx}$. $P(x)$ is the coefficient of y so in this case, $P(x) = 1$. Solve $\dfrac{dy}{dx} + y = 2x$ by this method and verify the result in example 1.

2. The differential equation $(4x + t - 7)dt + (8x^2 + 4t)dx = 0$ in example 2 is called **exact** because the partial derivative of $(4x + t - 7)$ with respect to x is equal to the partial derivative of $(8x^2 + 4t)$ with respect to t. Solve this equation using the method of solving first-order exact differential equations.

3. The differential equation $\frac{dx}{dt} = (x-1)^2$, $x(0) = 1.1$ is separable. Solve it using the method of separating variables and then check your result using desolve.

4. What happens if the initial condition in problem 3 is changed to $x(0)=1$?

5. The differential equation $(t^2 + x^2)dt + (t^2 - tx)dx = 0$ is called **homogeneous**. Solve it using the method of solving homogeneous first-order differential equations and then check your answer using desolve.

6. Certain methods for solving first-order differential equations involve making subtle substitutions and desolve cannot be used on them. Consider the differential equation $t\frac{dx}{dt} - x = \frac{t^3}{x}e^{x/t}$. Solve this equation by letting $u = \frac{x}{t}$.

7. A **Bernoulli equation** is one of the form $\frac{dx}{dt} + P(t)x = f(t)x^n$. It is solved by making the substitution $w = x^{1-n}$ so that the equation becomes linear in w. Solve $\frac{dx}{dt} + x = tx^4$ using this substitution and check it with desolve.

Mathematical Background: There are a variety of techniques for solving the various types of first-order differential equations. We include some types below. In each case the dependent variable is x and the independent variable is t.

A **separable differential equation** is one of the form $\frac{dx}{dt} = \frac{g(t)}{h(x)}$.

A **homogeneous differential equation** is one of the form $M(t,x)dt + N(t,x)dx = 0$ where M and N are homogeneous functions of the same degree.

An **exact differential equation** is one of the form $M(t,x)dt + N(t,x)dx = 0$ where $\frac{\partial M}{\partial x} = \frac{\partial N}{\partial t}$

A differential equation of the form $\frac{dx}{dt} + P(t)x = f(t)$ is called **a linear first order differential equation** (linear in x). It is solved by multiplying by an integrating factor, $e^{\int P(t)dt}$.

Program Syntax: There is no program for this exploration. However, we use the deSolve command from the Calculus menu: deSolve(equation,invar,depvar).

NOTES

Using deSolve for Second Order Differential Equations

Example 1   Use deSolve to solve the second order homogeneous with constant co-efficients: $x'' + 5x' + 6x = 0$.

Solution: The equation is entered along with an independent variable (we chose *t*) and the dependent variable, *x*.

We choose to write the solution as $x(t) = c_1 e^{-2t} + c_2 e^{-3t}$

Example 2   Use deSolve to solve the second order initial value problem:

$$x'' + 5x' + 6x = 6t - 2, \quad x(0) = -2 \text{ and } x'(0) = \frac{7}{2}.$$

Solution: The problem and its solution appear in the screen below:

The solution to $x'' + 5x' + 6x = 6t - 2$, $x(0) = -2$ and $x'(0) = \dfrac{7}{2}$ is $x(t) = \dfrac{-5e^{-3t}}{6} + t - \dfrac{7}{6}$.

Example 3   A lead weight with mass 0.1 slug is attached to the end of a spring that has a spring constant 2 lb/ft. The system is immersed in a medium that imparts a damping force numerically equal to 40% of the instantaneous velocity. From a position 1 foot above the equilibrium position, the lead weight is released from rest. Find the equation of motion and determine the first time the weight passes through the equilibrium position heading upward.

Solution: This problem is modeled by the following initial value problem:
$$0.1x'' + 0.4x' + 2x = 0, \quad x(0) = -1, x'(0) = 0.$$

```
■ deSolve(.1·x'' + .4·x' + 2·x = 0 and x(0)▶
    x = -e^(-2·t)·cos(4.·t) - .5·e^(-2·t)·sin(4.·t)
…and x(0)=-1 and x'(0)=0,t,x)
MAIN          RAD AUTO          FUNC 1/30
```

From the screen above, we see that the equation of motion is $x(t) = e^{-2t}\left(-\cos(4t) - \dfrac{1}{2}\sin(4t)\right)$

To answer the question, " the first time the weight passes through the equilibrium position heading upward", we graph the equation of motion.[1]

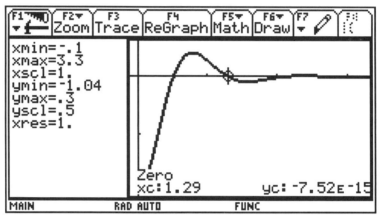

Using the "2:Zero" option of the Math menu, we find that the weight passes through the equilibrium position heading upward at about $t = 1.29$ seconds.

More analytically, we need to solve the equation

$x(t) = e^{-2t}\left(-\cos(4t) - \dfrac{1}{2}\sin(4t)\right) = 0$ the first time its derivative is negative.

(The derivative must be negative because the weight is going from positive position values to negative position values.) After using the zeros command (we could have also used the solve command) and replacing the arbitrary integer with the value of "2", we see 1.29 seconds in the screen below:

```
■ zeros(y1(t), t)
        {.785398163397·(@n7 - .35241638235)}
■ {.78539816339745·(2 - .35241638234957)}
                                {1.29400914735}
```

_____

[1] Of course, we have to enter the motion equation in the Y= editor as a function of x:

```
F1▼   F2▼  F3  F4  F5▼  F6▼
▼↙ Zoom Edit  ✓  All Style ▶◀ …
▲PLOTS
✓y1=e^(-2·x)·(-cos(4·x) - 1/2·sin(4·x))|x≥0
 y2=
```

Problems:

1. Suppose a 16-pound weight stretches a spring 32 inches in an environment that offers a damping force numerically equal to ½ the instantaneous velocity. Also assume the weight is released from rest two feet below the equilibrium position and is driven by an outside force $f(t) = 10\cos(3t)$. These conditions are modeled by the differential equation $\frac{1}{2}x'' + \frac{1}{2}x' + 6x = 10\cos(3t)$, $x(0) = 2$, $x'(0) = 0$. Use deSolve to find the equation of motion.

2. Graph the equation of motion found in problem 1 and compare it with the graph of Example 3 (where conditions were similar except for no impressed outside force). Explain the behavior of each equation of motion as t gets large.

3. a) Solve the differential equation $x'' + 16x = 12\cos(3t)$, $x(0) = 0$ and $x'(0) = 0$.

   b) Show that the solution found in part a) is equivalent to $x(t) = \frac{12}{7}\left(\cos(3t) - \cos(4t)\right)$

   c) Graph the solution.

4. a) Solve the initial value problem: $x'' + 16x = 12\cos(3.9t)$, $x(0) = 0$ and $x'(0) = 0$.

   b) Graph the solution for $0 \le t \le 80\pi$. Notice the oscillations, called **beats**, occur with frequency 40π. On the same axes, graph $x(t) = \pm\frac{12}{.39}\sin(.05t)$. These two functions are called the **envelope** of the solution.

Mathematical Background: A second order linear homogeneous differential equation with constant coefficients has the form $ax'' + bx' + cx = 0$ where x is a function of t. Solutions can be found by solving the associated auxiliary quadratic equation $am^2 + bm + c = 0$ that has roots $r_1 = \frac{-b + \sqrt{b^2 - 4ac}}{2a}$ and $r_2 = \frac{-b - \sqrt{b^2 - 4ac}}{2a}$. If $b^2 - 4ac > 0$ then the general solution to the differential equation is $x(t) = c_1 e^{r_1 t} + c_2 e^{r_2 t}$. If $b^2 - 4ac = 0$ then $r_1 = r_2$ and the general solution to the differential equation is $x(t) = c_1 e^{r_1 t} + c_2 t e^{r_1 t}$. If $b^2 - 4ac < 0$ then, with $r_1 = \alpha + \beta i$ and $r_2 = \alpha - \beta i$, the general solution to the differential equation can be written as $x(t) = e^{\alpha t}\left(c_1 \cos(\beta t) + c_2 \sin(\beta t)\right)$. Higher order linear homogeneous differential equations can be solved in a similar fashion.

To solve a second order linear ***non***-homogeneous differential equation with constant coefficients, like $ax'' + bx' + cx = f(t)$, we first find x_c, a solution to the complementary homogeneous equation and then find x_p, a particular solution to the non-homogeneous equation. The general solution then takes the form $x(t) = x_c + x_p$. There are other methods of solution as well.

Program Syntax: There is no program for this exploration. However, we use the deSolve command from the Calculus menu: deSolve(equation,invar,depvar).

Exploration #12

Using the Program diffq() to Solve Differential Equations: Part 1.

The provided program *diffq()* offers a wide range of additional methods for solving differential equations. Any differential equation of order greater than two, for example, cannot be solved using the command deSolve. The program has many features. We will illustrate several of them in this exploration and the next.

Upon running diffq(), we obtain the following five menu options:

Each of the first three of these menus has several options as shown below:

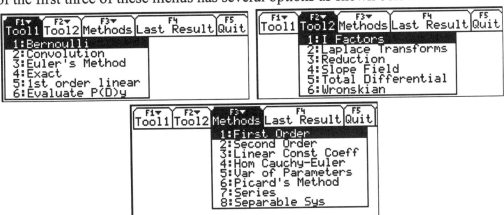

Example 1. Bernoulli. A first order differential equation of the form
$y' + p(x) \cdot y = f(x) \cdot y^n$ is called a ***Bernoulli equation*** and is in a class of first order differential equations that require a substitution for solution. Use diffq() to solve: $y' + \frac{1}{x} \cdot y = x \cdot y^2$.

Solution: The solution is displayed below. It is also stored in the variable location named ***answer.***

This solution is often written as $y = \frac{-1}{x(x-c)}$.

Example 2. Exact Equations. A first order differential equation of the form $M(x,y)dx + N(x,y)dy = 0$ is exact provided $\frac{\partial M}{\partial y} = \frac{\partial N}{\partial x}$. Verify that $\left(y^2 - 1\right)dx + 2xy\ dy = 0$ is exact before using diffq() to solve it.

Solution: Since $\frac{\partial M}{\partial y} = 2y$ and $\frac{\partial N}{\partial x} = 2y$, the equation is exact. The solution is found by interpreting the output below:

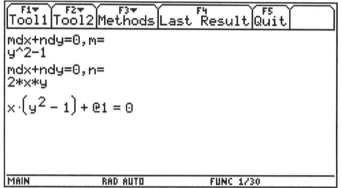

The solution to $\left(y^2 - 1\right)dx + 2xy\ dy = 0$ is $x\cdot\left(y^2 - 1\right) + c_1 = 0$ or equivalently

$$x\cdot\left(y^2 - 1\right) = c.$$

The function $x\cdot\left(y^2 - 1\right)$ that is returned has the property that its *total differential* is the left-hand side of the original differential equation. Since that total differential is zero, the solution is found by setting the returned function equal to a constant. ■

Example 3. Differential Operators. The sixth option under the $\boxed{\text{F1}}$ Tools1 menu is used to evaluate a differential operator of a function of x. Use this option to show that the differential operator $D^2 + 2D + 5$ annihilates (that is, evaluates to zero) the function $5e^{-x}\cos(2x) - 7e^{-x}\sin(2x)$.

Solution:

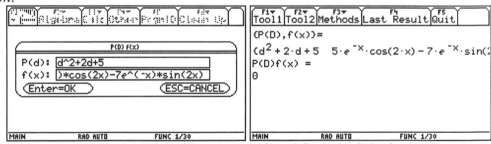

Left: We enter the differential operator $(P(d))$ and $f(x)$ in the dialog box.
Right: The evaluation is returned and, since the result is zero, we say that $P(d)$ annihilates $f(x)$. ■

Example 4. Laplace Transforms. Use diffq() to find the following Laplace transforms: a) $\mathcal{L}\left(\sin\left(3t\right)\right)$ b) $\mathcal{L}\left(e^{5t}t^3\right)$.

Solution: The Laplace transform is the second option under the ▣ Tool2 menu. The results of invoking it for each function are shown below:

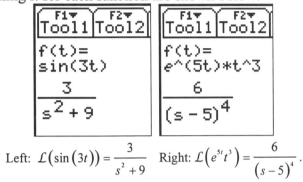

Left: $\mathcal{L}\left(\sin\left(3t\right)\right) = \dfrac{3}{s^2 + 9}$ Right: $\mathcal{L}\left(e^{5t}t^3\right) = \dfrac{6}{\left(s-5\right)^4}$.   ■

Example 5. Reduction of Order. If one solution to a differential equation[1] is known, the reduction of order formula can be used to find a second, linearly independent solution to the differential equation. Find that second solution to $y'' - 6y' + 9y = 0$ knowing that one solution is $y_1 = e^{3x}$.

Solution: The second solution is returned as $y_2 = xe^{3x}$.

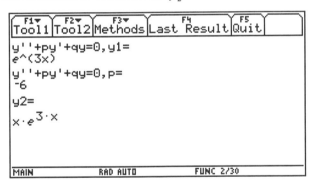

     ■

Example 6. The Wronskian. Use the Wronskian tool to determine whether or not each of these collections of functions is linearly independent:

     a) $\left\{e^{2x}, e^{3x}, e^{-2x}\right\}$ b) $\left\{1+x, 1-x, 2x\right\}$ c) $\left\{1-x, 5+x^2, 2x^2 - x\right\}$

---

[1] The differential equation for this application is assumed to be a second order linear homogeneous differential equation of the form $y'' + p(x)y' + q(x)y = 0$.

Solution: $\{e^{2x}, e^{3x}, e^{-2x}\}$ is a collection of linearly independent functions as is $\{1-x, 5+x^2, 2x^2-x\}$ because in either case, their Wronskian evaluates to a non-zero quantity. The collection $\{1+x, 1-x, 2x\}$ is linearly dependent because its Wronskian is 0. See the output screens below.

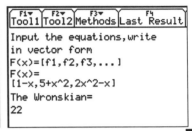

Problems:

1.   a) Solve the Bernoulli equation: $x^2 y' - 2xy = 3y^4$.
       b) Solve the above equation with the initial condition $y(1) = .5$

2.   Use the convolution option of the ⒡ Tool1 menu to find the convolution of $f(t) = \sin t$ and $g(t) = e^t$.

3.   Use the third option of the ⒡ Tool1 menu, Euler's Method, to approximate y when x is 1.5 given $y' = .1xy$, $y(1) = 1$ and h is 0.05. For this option, first enter the right hand side of the differential equation as f in the ⒡ menu. Here you will also be prompted for $x_0 = 1$, $y_0 = 1$, and $h = 0.05$. Show that $y(1.5) \approx 1.0630$.

4.   a) Show that $(5x + 4y)dx + (4x - y^2)dy = 0$ is exact.
       b) Find the general solution to $(5x + 4y)dx + (4x - y^2)dy = 0$.
       c) Solve the initial value problem: $(5x + 4y)dx + (4x - y^2)dy = 0$, $y(0) = 2$.

5.   a) Solve the linear differential equation $y' + y = f(x)$ where $f(x) = \begin{cases} 1, & 0 \le x \le 1 \\ 0, & x > 1 \end{cases}$ by using the fifth option of the ⒡ Tool1 menu. (Hint: Use it twice, once for each piece of f.)
       b) Additionally, assume the initial condition $y(0) = 0$. Express the solution as a piecewise function.
       c) If the solution to part b) is to be a continuous function, what must the solution be? (Hint: Consider the graph.)

6.   Evaluate $(D-2)^2 \left(4e^{2x} - 10xe^{2x} \right)$.

7.   Evaluate the following Laplace transforms:
       a) $\mathcal{L}\left(t^2 \right)$ b) $\mathcal{L}\left(3t - 4\cos(2t) \right)$

8.   a) It is known that $y_1 = x^2$ is a solution to the differential equation $y'' + \dfrac{2}{x} y' - \dfrac{6}{x^2} = 0$.
       Use reduction of order to find a second solution.
       b) What is the general solution to $y'' + \dfrac{2}{x} y' - \dfrac{6}{x^2} = 0$?

9.   Determine whether or not the collection $\left\{ x, e^x, xe^x \right\}$ is a collection of linearly independent functions.

10.   a) Use the Wronskian to show that the collection $\{1 - 2x, x + 3, 5\}$ is linearly dependent.
       b) Express $1 - 2x$ as a linear combination of the other two functions in the collection.

11.   If the left-hand side of the differential equation $M(x, y)dx + N(x, y)dy = 0$ is the **total differential** of a function f, then the differential equation is exact. Furthermore, the solution to the differential equation is $f(x, y) = c$. Use the option 5 of the ⒡ Tool2 menu to find the total differential of $f(x, y) = x \cdot \left(y^2 - 1 \right)$. Compare this with the differential equation in Example 2.

Mathematical Background: Much of the mathematical background necessary for this exploration has been presented in the previous two explorations and will not be repeated here.

The **Laplace transform** of a function $f(t)$ is given by $\mathcal{L}(f(t)) = \int_0^\infty e^{-st} f(t)dt$ and is a function of s. The Laplace transform is used to solve differential equations.

A collection of n functions is said to be linearly independent if none of the functions can be written as a linear combination of the others. That is a difficult property to test especially for large collections of functions. An equivalent test is to evaluate the collection's **Wronskian**. For the collection $\{f_1, f_2, \ldots f_n\}$, the Wronskian is given by the following determinant:

$$\begin{vmatrix} f_1 & f_2 & \cdots & f_n \\ f_1' & f_2' & \cdots & f_n' \\ \vdots & \cdots & \ddots & \vdots \\ f_1^{(n-1)} & f_2^{(n-1)} & \cdots & f_n^{(n-1)} \end{vmatrix}$$

Program Syntax: The program for this exploration is a menu-driven program to handle a variety of tools and methods for solving differential equation. By typing diffq() on the edit line of the home screen, the program immediately shows its five menu options. The program diffq() takes no parameters. For convenience, it stores the results of calculations in the location *answer*.

Exploration #13
Using the Program diffq() to Solve Differential Equations: Part 2.

This second exploration involving the program ***diffq()*** will examine the methods ([F3])
option within the program. There are eight selections and we illustrate the first six in the examples that follow. The exercises address the last two selections.

Example 1. First Order. Solve: $y' = \sqrt{x - 2y + 3}$.

Solution: The solution of this differential equation can be found by making the substitution $u = x - 2y + 3$ making it separable in u and y. We can enter it directly, however, in this program.

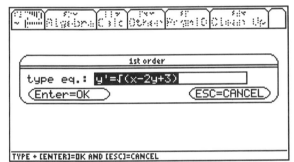
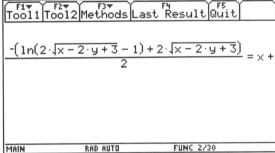

Left: The equation is entered.
Right: The solution is displayed but scrolls off the I/O output screen. For that reason we choose [F4] Last Result
to see that, when the equation is viewed from the home screen, the right hand side is actually " $x + @1$ ".

∎

Example 2. Second Order. Use diffq() to solve the initial value problem:

$$2y'' - 4y' + 2y = \frac{e^x}{x}, \quad y(1) = e, \ y'(1) = e .$$

Solution: We choose the "with initial conditions" option:

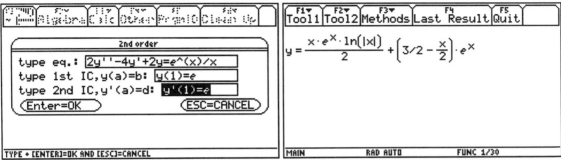

Left: The equation and initial conditions are entered. Right: The solution is displayed.

The solution to $2y''- 4y'+2y = \dfrac{e^x}{x}$, $y(1) = e$, $y'(1) = e$ is $y = \dfrac{x \cdot e^x \cdot \ln|x|}{2} + \left(3/2 - \dfrac{x}{2}\right)e^x$.

Example 3. Higher Order DEs with Constant Coefficients. Find the general solution to this fourth order linear differential equation with constant coefficients: $y^{(4)} - 2y'''+4y''-8y' = e^x$.

Solution: The related homogeneous equation is $y^{(4)} - 2y'''+4y''-8y' = 0$ and the characteristic (or auxiliary) equation is $m^4 - 2m^3 + 4m^2 - 8m = 0$

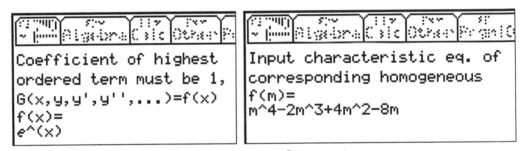

Left: The function e^x is entered.
Right: The left hand side of the characteristic equation (a function of *m*) is entered.

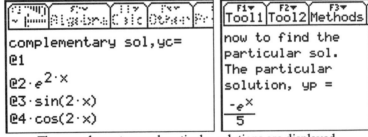

The complementary and particular solutions are displayed.

Thus the general solution is $y = c_1 + c_2 e^{2x} + c_3 \sin(2x) + c_4 \cos(2x) - \dfrac{e^x}{5}$

Example 4. Homogeneous Cauchy-Euler Equations. Solve the differential equation $2x^2 y'' + 7xy' - 3y = 0$.

Solution: Option 4 of the ⬚ Methods prompts you to enter the equation. We do so below. Notice the way the program expects derivatives to be entered:

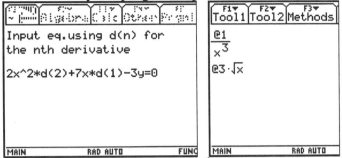

Left: The equation is entered with the nth derivative entered as $d(n)$.

Right: The two fundamental solutions are listed. Thus, the general solution is $y = c_1 x^{-3} + c_2 \sqrt{x}$.

Example 5. Variation of Parameters. Use diffq() to solve $y'' + 2y' + y = e^{-x} \ln x$.

Solution: This segment of the program uses the variation of parameters method and before we can proceed we must recognize that the corresponding homogeneous equation ($y'' + 2y' + y = 0$) has (fundamental, independent) solutions $c_1 e^{-x}$ and $c_2 x e^{-x}$. Now, with $f(x) = e^{-x} \ln x$, we are ready to proceed.

The coefficient of the highest ordered term must be 1 before selecting f(x) G(x,y,y',y'',...)=f(x) f(x)= e^(-x)*ln(x)	Input the solutions of the corresponding homogenoues equation as [y1,y2,y3,...,yn] = [e^(-x),x*e^(-x)]	The particular solution, yp = $\dfrac{x^2 \cdot (2 \cdot \ln(x) - 3) \cdot e^{-x}}{4}$

Left: We enter the $f(x)$. | Center: The two fundamental solutions to the corresponding differential equation are entered. | Right: The particular solution is returned

Thus the general solution is: $y = c_1 e^{-x} + c_2 x e^{-x} + \dfrac{x^2 \cdot (2 \ln x - 3) e^{-x}}{4}$.

Example 6. The Method of Successive Approximation (Picard Iteration). Perform three iterations to approximate the solution to the initial value problem: $y' = y^2$, $y(0) = 1$ and compare the approximation with the exact answer.

Solution: We leave it to the reader to determine the solution to be $y = \dfrac{-1}{x-1}$ and that solution can only pertain to an open interval **not** containing $x = 1$. Let's consider it on the interval $(0,1)$. Using Picard's successive approximation method, we obtain the screens below:

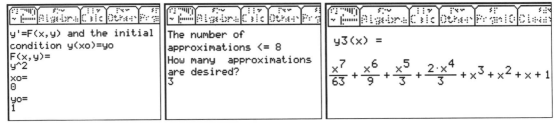

Left: The initial value problem   Center: We choose 3 iterations.   Right: The result of the third iteration
       is entered.   is displayed.

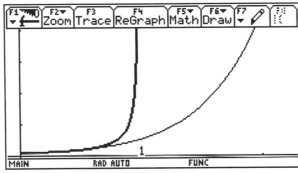

The exact solution, $y = \dfrac{-1}{x-1}$ is plotted in thick style and the seventh degree approximation
(which is reasonably close on (0, 1)) is plotted in line style.

Problems:

1.   a) In the study of population dynamics, the so-called **logistic equation**
$\dfrac{dP}{dt} = P \cdot (a - bP)$ is found. Find the general solution to the first order differential
equation: $y' = y\left(10^{-1} - 10^{-7}y\right)$ and check your answer using diffq().

   b) Use diffq() to solve the initial value problem: $y' = y\left(10^{-1} - 10^{-7}y\right)$, $y(0) = 5000$.

   c) Graph your solution to part b). What is the limit of y (the population) as the independent variable (t, time) grows without bound?

2.   a) In the study of series circuits, an LRC (a circuit with inductance, resistance, and
capacitance) is modeled by $L\dfrac{d^2q}{dt^2} + R\dfrac{dq}{dt} + \dfrac{1}{C}q = E(t)$ where L is inductance (meas-

ured in henrys), R is resistance (measured in ohms), C is capacitance (measured in farads), E is an impressed voltage on the system and $q(t)$ is the charge (in coulombs) on the capacitor at any time t. Further, the current (in amperes) in the circuit is $i(t) = q'(t)$. Use diffq() to find $q(t)$ for a system where $L = \frac{1}{4}$ henry, $R = 10$ ohms, $C = 0.001$ farad and the impressed voltage on the system is given by $E(t) = 5\sin(60.1t)$.

b) Assume $q(0) = 1$ and $q'(0) = i(0) = 0$. What is the solution to the complementary differential equation, $q_c(t)$? (This is called the **transient solution** to the system.)

c) What is the particular solution to the system, $q_p(t)$? (This is called the **steady-state solution**.)

3. Use the third option of the ⊞ Methods menu of diffq() to solve the fourth order differential equation $y^{(4)} + 2y''' - 2y' - y = e^x$.

4. Use the fourth option of the ⊞ Methods menu of diffq() to solve the Cauchy-Euler differential equation $4x^2 y'' + 8xy' + y = 0$.

5. Use the fifth option of the ⊞ Methods menu of diffq() to solve $y'' + y = 1 - \sin^2 x$.

6. Re-examine example 6 and find five iterations. Graph $y3$, $y4$, $y5$ and observe their relation with the exact solution.

7. a) Find the exact solution to $y' = (y-1)^2$, $y(1) = 0$.

b) Use Picard iteration to find the first three approximations.
c) Graph $y0$, $y1$, $y2$, $y3$ along with your answer to part a).
d) Over what open interval is the approximation "close"?

8. a) Solve $y'' - 3y' + 2 = 0$ either in your head or with paper and pencil.

b) Use the seventh option of the ⊞ Methods menu of diffq() to find a series approximation (use six terms) to this differential equation.[1]
c) Describe the relationship between your result in part b) and the Maclaurin series of your answer to part a).

9. Solve the separable differential equation $y'''' = -\sin(x) + \cos(x)$ with the system of

initial conditions: $\begin{cases} y'''(0) = 7 \\ y''(0) = -1 \\ y'(0) = -1 \\ y(0) = 0 \end{cases}$ using the eighth option of the ⊞ Methods menu of

diffq(). (Some books refer to this as a **separable system**.)

---

[1] The differential equation has to be entered in differential operator notation. See the screen below:

```
        Differential Operators:P(d)y=0
 ┌─────────────────────────────────────┐
 │ P(d)=: d^2-3d+2                       │
 │ # of terms=: 6                       │
 │ (Enter=OK)            (ESC=CANCEL)    │
 └─────────────────────────────────────┘
```

Mathematical Background: Much of the mathematical background necessary for this exploration has been presented in the previous three explorations and will not be repeated here.

A second order linear homogeneous differential equation with constant coefficients has the form $ax'' + bx' + cx = 0$ where x is a function of t. Solutions can be found by solving the associated auxiliary quadratic equation $am^2 + bm + c = 0$ that has roots $r_1 = \dfrac{-b + \sqrt{b^2 - 4ac}}{2a}$ and $r_2 = \dfrac{-b - \sqrt{b^2 - 4ac}}{2a}$. If these coefficients are not constants but are functions of t corresponding to the order of the term we have $at^2 x'' + btx' + cx = 0$, called the *second order homogeneous Caucy-Euler equation.* (Some books call this an *equidimensional equation* and others refer to it simply as an *Euler equation.*) The method of solution is to create the so-called *indicial equation* $am^2 + (b - a)m + c = 0$.

The method called *variation of parameters* is useful in solving differential equations of the form $y'' + p(x)y' + q(x)y = f(x)$. If $y_1(x)$ and $y_2(x)$ are fundamental solutions to the homogeneous equation $y'' + p(x)y' + q(x)y = 0$ then we begin by finding two functions, $u_1(x)$ and $u_2(x)$ that satisfy $\begin{cases} u'_1 y_1 + u'_2 y_2 = 0 \\ u'_1 y'_1 + u'_2 y'_2 = f(x) \end{cases}$. Then, $y_p = u_1 y_1 + u_2 y_2$ is a particular solution to $y'' + p(x)y' + q(x)y = f(x)$.

Picard's method of successive approximation is a way of approximating the solution y to the differential equation $y' = f(x, y)$ at (x_0, y_0) with a function y_n. A first approximation is $y_1 = y_0 + \int_{x_0}^{x} f(x, y_0)\,dx$ and then a second approximation is obtained by replacing y_0 with y_1 in the integrand: $y_1 = y_0 + \int_{x_0}^{x} f(x, y_1)\,dx$ and so on.

A separable differential equation, such as $y'''' = -\sin(x) + \cos(x)$, together with a system of initial conditions, like $\begin{cases} y'''(0)=7 \\ y''(0)=-1 \\ y'(0)=-1 \\ y(0)=0 \end{cases}$, is sometimes referred to as a *separable system.*

Program Syntax: The program for this exploration is a menu-driven program to handle a variety of tools and methods for solving differential equation. By typing diffq() on the edit line of the home screen, the program immediately shows its five menu options. This exploration concentrated on the F3 Methods menu of diffq(). For convenience (and in cases where output scrolls off the screen), the program stores the results of calculations in the location *answer*.

Exploration #14
Vectors and Vector Calculus

Example 1. Operations with Vectors. Suppose $\vec{A} = [1, 2, -5]$ and $\vec{B} = [2, -3, 0]$.

Use the program vectdisp() to find:
a) The length (or ***norm***) of each vector
b) The dot product of A with B
c) The cross product $\vec{A} \times \vec{B}$ and the norm of the cross product
d) The angle between $\vec{A}$ and $\vec{B}$
e) The projection of $\vec{A}$ onto $\vec{B}$ and the projection of $\vec{B}$ onto $\vec{A}$.

Solution: Upon running vectdisp(), `■vectdisp([1 2 -5],[2 -3 0])`, we are prompted to choose exact or approximate results. We choose exact and display the output of the screens below:

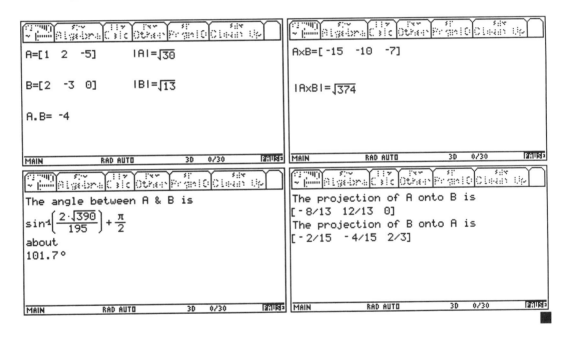

Example 2. Planes(). Find the distance between the line expressed parametrically as
$x = -2t$
$y = -2 + 3t$ and the point (-1, 3, 4).
$z = 1 + 4t$

Solution: The program Planes() can be found as the seventh option under F1 Math1 in the CUST89() custom menu system. The program actually creates another custom menu system.

To find the distance between a point and a line, we select the "ptlin" option of the planes() menu.[1]

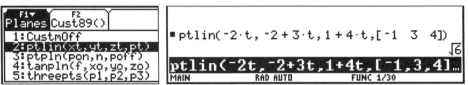

Left: The planes() options. Right: The distance between the line and the point is $\sqrt{6}$ units.

We point out here that if we wanted to find the distance between a line and a point in two dimensions (in the xy plane), simply let the z coordinate of the point and zt both be zero.

∎

Example 3. Directional Derivatives and Gradients. For the function
$$f(x,y) = y^2 e^x,$$ find the maximum value of a directional derivative at $(0,-2)$ and give a unit vector in the direction of that maximum.

Solution: The maximum value of a directional derivative will be the norm of the gradient at the point. The function delpo() (found as the fourth option under [F2] Math2 of the CUST89() custom menu) returns the gradient (also known as the *del* function) of a function at a point. Notice in the screen below that the z values are set to zero. This is because the delpo() function allows input for functions of three variables (as does the related function dirder()).

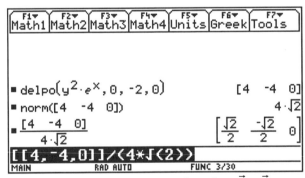

Interpret line 1 above as $\nabla f(0,-2) = 4\vec{i} - 4\vec{j}$.

Interpret line 3 as the unit vector $\dfrac{\nabla f(0,-2)}{\|\nabla f(0,-2)\|} = \dfrac{\sqrt{2}}{2}\vec{i} - \dfrac{\sqrt{2}}{2}\vec{j}$

Finally, we verify that the value of the directional derivative is in fact $4\sqrt{2}$ by invoking dirder() as seen below:

---

[1] The other options of the planes() menu are: ptpln (for finding the distance between a point and a plane), tanpln (for finding the equation of a plane tangent to a surface at a point), and threepts (for finding the equation of a plane given three points).

$$\bullet \text{dirder}\left(y^2 \cdot e^x, [0 \ \ -2 \ \ 0], \left[\frac{\sqrt{2}}{2} \ \ \frac{-\sqrt{2}}{2} \ \ 0\right]\right)$$
$$4 \cdot \sqrt{2}$$
...0,-2,0],[J(2)/2,-J(2)/2,0])
MAIN   RAD AUTO   FUNC 4/30

Example 4. Curvature and Torsion. Consider the function $r(t) = t\vec{\mathbf{i}} + \frac{t^2}{2}\vec{\mathbf{j}} + \frac{t^3}{3}\vec{\mathbf{k}}$.

Find the curvature and torsion at the point $t = 0$

Solution: Option 1 of the F3 Math3 menu will run the program curtor(). We obtain the following output:

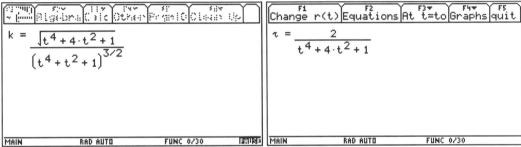

Left: The general expression for curvature appears. Right: The expression for torsion.

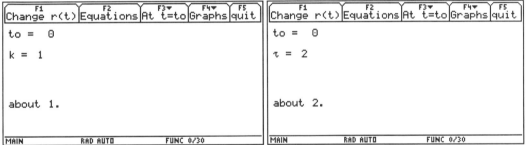

We see that at $t = 0$ we have $\kappa = 1$ and $\tau = 2$.

We point out that in the previous example, we could have opted to see the graphs of the expressions representing curvature or torsion. It is the F4 option in the program. We display them below:

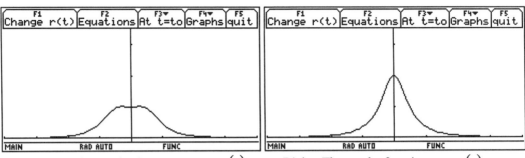

Left: The graph of curvature t vs $\kappa(t)$.　　Right: The graph of torsion t vs $\tau(t)$.

Problems:

In questions 1 through 4, use the program vectdisp() to find　a) $\left\|\vec{A}\right\|$　b) $\left\|\vec{B}\right\|$　c) $\vec{A}\cdot\vec{B}$

　d) $\vec{A}\times\vec{B}$　e) the angle between $\vec{A}$ and $\vec{B}$　f) the projection of $\vec{A}$ onto $\vec{B}$　and

　g) the projection of $\vec{B}$ onto $\vec{A}$.

1. $\vec{A}=[1,\text{-}5]$ and $\vec{B}=[3,1]$

2. $\vec{A}=[1,\text{-}5,6]$ and $\vec{B}=[0,-2,1]$

3. $\vec{A}=[3,\text{-}1,0]$ and $\vec{B}=[-2,-2,7]$

4. $\vec{A}=2\vec{i}+\vec{j}-\vec{k}$ and $\vec{B}=\vec{i}+2\vec{j}+\vec{k}$

5. The vectors from two dimensional space in question 1 above can actually be plotted along with their sum, $\vec{A}+\vec{B}$. Use the program vecplot() to verify the result below:

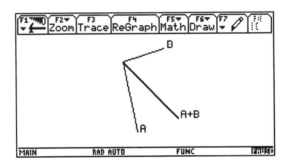

Questions 6 through 9 all refer to options within the planes() menu system.

6. Find the distance between the line expressed parametrically as $\begin{array}{l}x=1+t\\y=3-t\\z=2t\end{array}$ and the point

　$(1,1,5)$.

7. Use ptpln() to find the distance between the point $(1,1,3)$ and the plane $3x + 2y + 6z = 6$.

(Hint: You will need to enter this as ptpln([x0,y0,z0],[3,2,6],[1,1,3]) where x0, y0, z0 are the coordinates of any point on the plane.)

8. Use tanpln() to find the equation of the plane tangent to the surface $z = 9 - x^2 - y^2$ at the point (1, 2, 4). (Hint: You will need to enter this as tanpln($x^2 + y^2 + z - 9$, 1, 2, 4).)

9. Use threepts() to find the equation of the plane containing (1,3,3), (-3,4,9/2), and (7,0,0).

10. Find the directional derivative of $f(x,y) = x^3 - 2y^2 + 3$ at the point (2, 1) in the direction of the vector $\left[-\sqrt{3}, 1 \right]$.

11. Suppose $f(x,y) = xy \sin(yz)$.

a) Find the directional derivative of f at the point $(-2, 1, \pi)$ in the direction of the vector $[3, -2, -5]$.

b) Evaluate the gradient of f at the point $(-2, 1, \pi)$.

12. Show that neither the curvature nor the torsion are dependent upon t for the helix given by $r(t) = (2\cos t)\vec{\mathbf{i}} + (2\sin t)\vec{\mathbf{j}} + 3t\vec{\mathbf{k}}$ by finding each.

Mathematical Background: The *length* or *norm* of an n-dimensional vector $\vec{v} = [v_1, v_2, \ldots v_n]$

is $\|\vec{v}\| = \sqrt{\sum_{i=1}^{n} v_i^2}$. A vector is said to be *normalized* if it has the form $\dfrac{1}{\|\vec{v}\|}\vec{v}$, a vector in the

direction of $\vec{v}$ with length 1 (or *unit vector*). In 3-space, there are three special unit vectors, each in the direction of the coordinate axes of the rectangular coordinate system, $\vec{\mathbf{i}} = [1,0,0], \vec{\mathbf{j}} = [0,1,0]$, and $\vec{\mathbf{k}} = [0,0,1]$ and every vector can be written as a linear combination of these. For example, $\vec{v} = [-3, 5, 10] = -3\vec{\mathbf{i}} + 5\vec{\mathbf{j}} + 10\vec{\mathbf{k}}$.

The *dot product* of two non-zero vectors is defined to be $\vec{\mathbf{u}} \cdot \vec{\mathbf{v}} = \|u\|\|v\|\cos\theta$ where θ is the angle between the two vectors. In 2-space, if $\vec{\mathbf{u}} = [u_1, u_2]$ and $\vec{v} = [v_1, v_2]$, then $\vec{\mathbf{u}} \cdot \vec{v} = u_1 v_1 + u_2 v_2$. If the dot product of two non-zero vectors is 0, then the angle between them must be $90°$ and the vectors are said to be *orthogonal*.

For vector component of $\vec{u}$ projected onto $\vec{v}$ (or in the direction of $\vec{v}$) is

$\text{proj}_{\vec{v}}\vec{u} = \dfrac{\vec{u}\bullet\vec{v}}{\left\|\vec{v}\right\|^2}\vec{v}$. The dot product of two vectors is a scalar quantity but the *cross product* of

two vectors, defined as, $\vec{u}\times\vec{v} = \begin{vmatrix} u_2 & u_3 \\ v_2 & v_3 \end{vmatrix}\vec{i} - \begin{vmatrix} u_1 & u_3 \\ v_1 & v_3 \end{vmatrix}\vec{j} + \begin{vmatrix} u_1 & u_2 \\ v_1 & v_2 \end{vmatrix}\vec{k}$ is a vector. This definition, in

3-space, is applied to $\vec{u} = [u_1, u_2, u_3]$ and $\vec{v} = [v_1, v_2, v_3]$.

The ***directional derivative*** of a function f in the direction of unit vector $\vec{u}$ at the point (x_0, y_0) is given by $D_{\vec{u}}f(x_0, y_0) = f_x(x_0, y_0)u_1 + f_y(x_0, y_0)u_2$. The ***gradient*** of f is defined by $\nabla f(x, y) = f_x\vec{i} + f_y\vec{j}$. The dot product of the gradient of f with a unit vector $\vec{u}$ yields the directional derivative of f in the direction of $\vec{u}$.

Curvature (κ) is a measure of the "bend" of a curve and can be defined in several equivalent ways. Here, we say that if a graph is defined by a vector function $\mathbf{r}(t)$, then $\kappa = \dfrac{\left\|\mathbf{r}'\times\mathbf{r}''\right\|}{\left\|\mathbf{r}'\right\|^3}$. ***Torsion*** (τ) can be computed as $\tau = \dfrac{[\mathbf{r}'\times\mathbf{r}'']\bullet\mathbf{r}'''}{\left\|\mathbf{r}'\times\mathbf{r}''\right\|^2}$ and is a measure of the amount of twisting along the curve.

Program Syntax: There are many programs and functions referenced in this exploration. The reader is urged to access them from the CUST89() custom menu system. There the syntax for calling a program (or function) is shown.

Exploration #15
Lagrange Multipliers

__Example 1__   Find the maximum rectangular area that can be enclosed using 23 ft of
fencing if fencing is required on only three of the four sides. (The fourth side
is bounded by a river.)[1]

Solution: The picture verifies that we are to maximize $f(x,y) = xy$ subject to the
constraint $2x + y = 23$ (or, equivalently, $g(x,y) = 23 - 2x - y$).

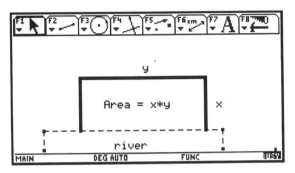

The program is invoked by entering $\text{lagrang}(x*y + \lambda*(23 - 2x - y), \{x, y, \lambda\})$.

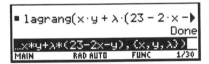

The output is displayed below. Note that both exact and approximate screens are
produced. We interpret the solution this way: the maximum area is obtained when
$x = 5.75$ ft and $y = 11.5$ ft ft. The maximum area is 66.125 ft^2 .

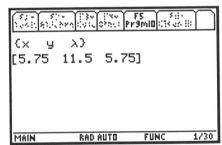 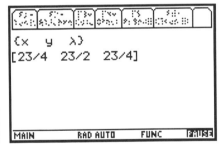

__Example 2__   Find the minimum distance the point (0, 5) is from the ellipse
$(x-4)^2 + 2y^2 = 4$.

---

[1] This example is adapted from Applied Calculus, Fourth Edition by Claudia Taylor and Lawrence Gilligan
(1996: Brooks/Cole, Pacific Grove).

Solution: As we can see from the screen below, we must minimize

$$f(x,y) = \sqrt{x^2 + (y-5)^2} \text{ subject to } (x-4)^2 + 2y^2 = 4$$

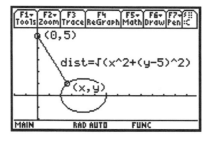

The program lagrang() is invoked by typing

$$\text{lagrang}\left(\sqrt{x^2 + (y-5)^2} + \lambda \cdot \left((x-4)^2 + 2y^2 - 4\right), \{x, y, \lambda\}\right).$$

It yields the output below:

```
{x    y    λ}
[2.63182  1.03153   .20198]
```

Interpretation: The distance $\sqrt{x^2 + (y-5)^2}$ is minimized when $x \approx 2.63$ and $y \approx 1.03$. That distance is about 4.76 units.

■

Finally, we point out that the program lagrang() works for functions of more than two independent variables. For example, to minimize $f(x,y,z) = x^2 + 2y^2 + 3z^2$, subject to $g(x,y,z) = 3x - 2y - 4z - 49$, we can enter:

$$\text{lagrang}\left(x^2 + 2y^2 + 3z^2 + \lambda \cdot (3x - 2y - 4z - 49), \{x, y, z, \lambda\}\right)$$

and observe that the solution occurs at $(9,-3,-4)$ and *f*'s minimum value is 147.

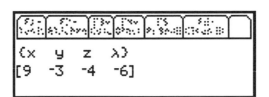

```
{x    y    z    λ}
[9   -3   -4   -6]
```

Problems:

1. Find the points on the graph of $y = 9 - x^2$ that are closest to the origin.

2. A rectangle is to be constructed so that the perimeter will be 80 inches. What is the maximum area for the rectangle?

3. Find the shortest distance between the curves $y^2 = x$ and $y = 2x + 4$.

4. A company, using the Cobb-Douglas model, estimates that its production level, P, is given by $P(x,y) = 100x^{0.4}y^{0.6}$ where x is the units of labor at \$200 each and y is the units of capital at \$300 each. The total expenditure for labor and capital is not to exceed \$50,000. Find the maximum production level subject to the appropriate constraint.

5. Find the minimum distance between the parabolas $y^2 = x$ and $y = (x+3)^2 - 1$.

Mathematical Background: The method of Lagrange multipliers is used to optimize a function $f(x,y)$ subject to the constraint $g(x,y) = 0$. Basic to the process is the introduction of the variable λ to create the function $F(x,y,\lambda) = f(x,y) + \lambda \cdot g(x,y)$ and then to set the three partial derivatives F_x, F_y, and F_λ, equal to zero.

Program Syntax: The program name is lagrange and it requires the parameters f, λ, g, x, and y in the following scheme: $\text{lagrang}(f + \lambda * g, \{x, y, \lambda\})$.

NOTES

Exploration #16
Fourier Series

Example 1   Use ten terms of a Fourier series to approximate the function $f(x) = x$ on the interval $-\pi \le x \le \pi$.

Solution: We choose to use the program fourier() to calculate and graph the approximation. The reader should verify that the (infinite) Fourier series is given by:

$$f(x) = \sum_{n=1}^{\infty} \frac{2}{n}(-1)^{n+1} \sin(nx).$$

Prior to running the program, we need to choose suitable window values. Note: with xscl set at 1, the graphing will be slower but more precise:

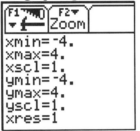

To begin, choose a suitable set of window values. The program will adjust xmin and xmax.

In this case, we want to find a complete Fourier series, so we choose the F1 menu option. Also, $p = \pi$ (p is half the length of the interval on which f is defined) and $n = 10$ (the number of terms with which we are approximating f). The program then prompts us for the function and the values of p and n. The results of the I/O screen and the graph appear below.

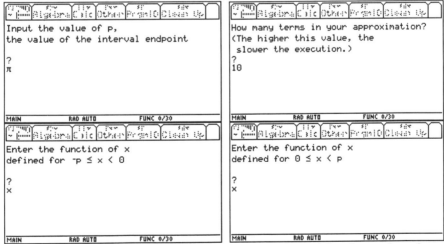

The fourier() set up screens. Upper left: the value of p is input. Upper right: the number of terms is entered. Lower left: the function definition for the interval $-p \le x < 0$. Lower right: the function for $0 \le x < p$

We observe that f is an odd function and its Fourier series is strictly a sine series. The series approximation is saved in the variable name "answer" for possible examination after quitting the program (since it scrolls off the screen in most cases).

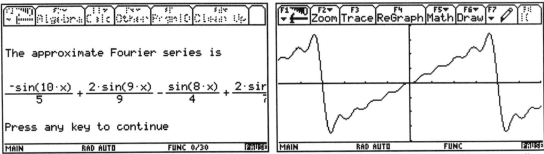

Left: Although the Fourier series scrolls off the screen, it has been saved in the variable "answer."
Right: The 10-term approximation is graphed. Note that it is periodic (with period 2π) and approximates $f(x) = x$ in the interval $-\pi < x < \pi$.

For the sake of comparison, we also ran the program to obtain a 25-term approximation. The graph appears below:

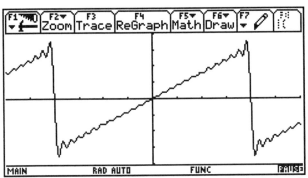

The 25-term Fourier series approximation for $f(x) = x$ in the interval $-\pi < x < \pi$. ■

Example 2 Expand the function $f(x) = x^2$ on $0 < x < \pi$ in a sine series. Use fifteen terms to approximate the function.

Solution: To expand in a sine series means that we extend f as an odd function on the interval $-\pi < x < 0$. We choose the program's F2 option.

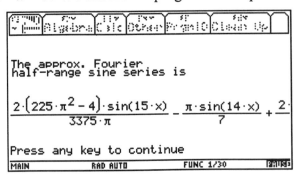

The reader should verify that the series is $\sum_{n=1}^{15}\left(\dfrac{2\cdot\left(2-\pi^2n^2\right)(-1)^n-4}{\pi n^3}\right)\left(\sin(nx)\right)$. The

fifteen –term approximation is graphed below:

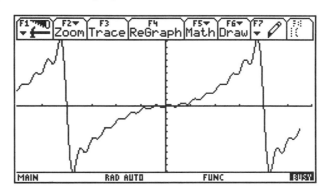

Example 3   Expand the function $f(x)=x^2$ on $0<x<\pi$ in a cosine series. Use fifteen terms to approximate the function.

Solution: To expand in a cosine series means that we extend f as an even function on the interval $-\pi<x<0$. We choose the program's F3 option and point out

that the series representation is given by $\dfrac{2\pi^2}{3}+\sum_{n=1}^{\infty}\left(\dfrac{4\cdot(-1)^n}{n^2}\right)\left(\cos(nx)\right)$. The

output and graph appear in the screens below:

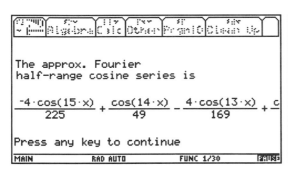
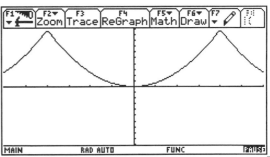

Problems: For questions 1 through 4, use the program fourier() to approximate the given function with a 10-term Fourier series on the given interval.

1. $f(x)=\begin{cases}0, & -\pi<x<0\\ 1, & 0\le x<\pi\end{cases}$

2. $f(x)=\begin{cases}0, & -1<x<0\\ 1, & 0\le x<1\end{cases}$

3. $f(x) = \begin{cases} 0, & -\pi < x < 0 \\ x^2, & 0 \le x < \pi \end{cases}$

4. $f(x) = x + \pi, \quad -\pi < x < \pi$

5. The function $f(x) = \begin{cases} -1, & -\pi < x < 0 \\ 1, & 0 \le x < \pi \end{cases}$ is an odd function. Show that its Fourier series is strictly a sine series and approximate it with 20 terms.

6. Find the half-range cosine expansion of $f(x) = \begin{cases} 1, & 0 < x < \frac{1}{2} \\ 0, & \frac{1}{2} \le x < 1 \end{cases}$ and graph the first 20 terms.

7. Find the half-range sine expansion of $f(x) = \begin{cases} 1, & 0 < x < \frac{1}{2} \\ 0, & \frac{1}{2} \le x < 1 \end{cases}$ and graph the first 20 terms.

8. Approximate $f(x) = x + 2$ on the interval $0 < x < 1$ in a fifteen term sine series.

9. Approximate $f(x) = x + 2$ on the interval $0 < x < 1$ in a fifteen term cosine series.

10. In Example 1, we saw a Fourier series for the function $f(x) = x$. Show that that series has the value of zero at every integer multiple of π.

11. a) Show that the Fourier series for $f(x) = x$ on the interval $0 < x < 2\pi$ is:
$$x = \pi - 2 \sum_{n=1}^{\infty} \frac{\sin(nx)}{n}$$
b) Show that the Fourier series for $f(x) = x^2$ on the interval $0 < x < 2\pi$ is:
$$x^2 = \frac{4\pi^2}{3} + 4 \sum_{n=1}^{\infty} \frac{\cos(nx)}{n^2} - 4\pi \sum_{n=1}^{\infty} \frac{\sin(nx)}{n}$$
c) Use parts a) and b) above to show that $\displaystyle\sum_{n=1}^{\infty} \frac{\sin(nx)}{n} = \frac{\pi - x}{2}$ and
$$\sum_{n=1}^{\infty} \frac{\cos(nx)}{n^2} = \frac{3x^2 - 6\pi x + 2\pi^2}{12}.$$

12. a) In Example 1 we saw $x = \displaystyle\sum_{n=1}^{\infty} \frac{2}{n}(-1)^{n+1} \sin(nx)$ on the interval $-\pi < x < \pi$. Show that on that same interval, $x^2 = \dfrac{\pi^2}{3} - 4 \displaystyle\sum_{n=1}^{\infty} (-1)^{n+1} \frac{\cos(nx)}{n^2}$.

b) Let x equal 0 in the expression $x^2 = \dfrac{\pi^2}{3} - 4\sum_{n=1}^{\infty}(-1)^{n+1}\dfrac{\cos(nx)}{n^2}$ from part a). Find a series representation for $\dfrac{\pi^2}{12}$.

c) Show that the Fourier sine series for $f(x) = 1$ is $\dfrac{4}{\pi}\sum_{n=1}^{\infty}\dfrac{\sin((2n-1)x)}{2n-1}$.

d) From part b) directly, show that $\dfrac{\pi}{4} = \sum_{n=1}^{\infty}\dfrac{\sin((2n-1)x)}{2n-1}$.

e) Use your result of part b) to create a numerical approximation for π . (Let $x = \dfrac{\pi}{2}$.)

Mathematical Background: If the function $f(x)$ is integrable[1] on the closed interval $[-p, p]$ then the ***Fourier series of f*** on $[-p, p]$ is given

by $\dfrac{a_0}{2} + \sum_{n=1}^{\infty}a_n\cos\left(\dfrac{n\pi}{p}x\right) + b_n\sin\left(\dfrac{n\pi}{p}x\right)$

where the coefficients are given by:

$$a_0 = \dfrac{1}{p}\int_{-p}^{p}f(x)\,dx \quad a_n = \dfrac{1}{p}\int_{-p}^{p}f(x)\cos\left(\dfrac{n\pi}{p}x\right)dx \quad b_n = \dfrac{1}{p}\int_{-p}^{p}f(x)\sin\left(\dfrac{n\pi}{p}x\right)dx$$

For practical purposes, we may choose a finite number of terms and form an approximation to (a possibly discontinuous function) f with a continuous finite series. If f is continuous, the series converges absolutely and uniformly to f. At a point of discontinuity of f, the series equals the arithmetic mean of the right-hand and left-hand limits at that point of discontinuity.

If f is an odd function, the a_i's are zero and we can write $b_n = \dfrac{2}{p}\int_{0}^{p}f(x)\sin\left(\dfrac{n\pi}{p}x\right)dx$.

If f is even, the b_i's are zero and we can write $a_n = \dfrac{2}{p}\int_{0}^{p}f(x)\cos\left(\dfrac{n\pi}{p}x\right)dx$.

A function defined on $[0, L]$ (rather than $[-p, p]$) can be approximated by extending it on $[-L, 0]$ to make it either even or odd. The resulting series is called a ***half-range expansion.*** See below:

---

[1] More precisely, the function f is a ***piecewise smooth*** function. That is, f and its first derivative are both continuous on $[-p, p]$ or they have only a finite number of jump discontinuities on $[-p, p]$. For a further discussion, the reader is urged to consult the book, *Fourier Series* by Georgi P. Tolstov, Dover Publications, ©1976.

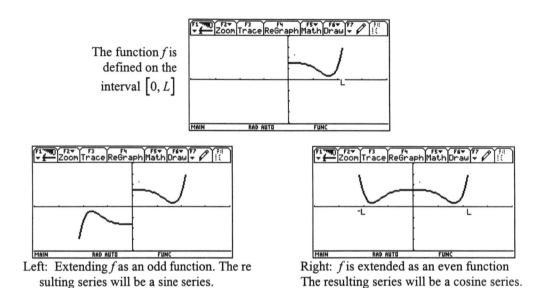

The function f is defined on the interval $[0, L]$

Left: Extending f as an odd function. The resulting series will be a sine series.

Right: f is extended as an even function The resulting series will be a cosine series.

Program Syntax: The program name is fourier and it prompts the user for f, p, and n where f is an expression in x, p is the semi-period, and n is the desired number of terms in the approximation. The n term Fourier approximation may likely scroll off the screen. If it does and you want to view it in its entirety, simply type "answer" from the HOME screen.

Program Listing

The next five pages comprise a listing of all programs and functions included on the accompanying diskette as well as the built-in TI-89/92-Plus commands which we have referenced in this text. ("Functions" are typically shorter routines that do not interact as much with the user and do not use the I/O screen; programs are longer and their output is to the I/O screen.)

Occasionally, an item is shaded which means that it was not directly referenced in the text so all such items will have a "N/A" for page reference.

Name	Program, function, or Command?	Necessary Input	Output	Page
arcl(xt,yt,zt,a,b)	Function	xt,yt,zt are the parametric parts of vector	the length of ard along the curve defined by the vecotr for t between a and b	N/A
arcLen(	Command	expression,var,left,right	the length of arc of expression from var=left to var=right	6
arearex()	Program	none but y1(x) and window values must be previously established	various graphing and calculation approximations to area under y1(x)	49-51
auxx(sols)	Program	sols is a row vector of solutions to the characteristic equation of a homogeneous linear equation with constant coefficients	solution to the homogeneous linear differential equation	N/A
avgRC(	Command	expression,var,[h]	forward difference quotient [as a function of h]	6
bern(p,f,n)	Function (called from diffq() program)	p, f, and n where y'+p(x)*y=f(x)*y^n	solution to the differential equation	81
caueul()	Program (called from diffq() program)	None. Program prompts for a homogeneous Cauchy-Euler differential equation	fundamental solutions	89
cfactor(	Command	expression, [var]	expression factored over complex numbers	2
Cmass()	Program	None. Upon execution, user is prompted for density function and coordinate system	center of mass (centroid) in either two or three dimensions	65-66
comDenom(	Command	expression, var	expression with a common denominator (if possible)	3, 4

Name	Program, func-tion, or Com-mand?	Necessary Input	Output	Page
Compstn(fu,gx,a)	Function	f is a function of u, g is a function of x, and a is an x-value	dy/dx evaluated at x=a	47
convol(f,g)	Function (called from diffq() pro-gram)	f and g are both functions of t	the convolution of f and g, f*g	84
curtor(xt,yt,zt)	Program	xt,yt,and zt are the para-metric components of a position vector	the general expressions for curvature and torsion, their graphs, as well as evalua-tions of them for a given value of t	95-96
CUST89()	Program	None	Creates an extremely con-venient custom menu sys-tem	28-29
czeros(	Command	expression, var	list of expression's complex zeros	3, 4
DA()	Program	None. Upon execution, user is prompted for func-tion and differential order	the double integral deter-mined by input	64
default()	Program	None	A utility program to set the calculator to default settings	N/A
defder()	Program	none	function, difference quo-tient, derivative	31-32
Define	Command	name = expression	Done (function is stored internally)	6
defn()	Program	none	This is a utility that installs or removes user-defined functions.	N/A
del(f,{vars})	Function	f is a function; {vars} is a list of variables found in f	a gradient vector	N/A
delpo(f,x0,y0,z0)	Function	f is a function of either two or three varibles and x0, y0, and z0 are coordi-nates of a point	the gradient at (x0,y0,z0)	94
deSolve(	Command	1st or 2nd order diff eq,indep var,dep var	general solution to diff eq	7, 73, 77
deSolve(	Command	1st or 2nd order diff eq and init cond,indep var,dep var	particular solution to diff eq	7, 74, 77-78
differentiate d(	Command	expression, var, [n]	n^{th} order derivative of ex-pression with respect to var	4
diffeval()	Program (called from diffq() pro-gram)	None. Program prompts user for differential op-erator P(d) and a function f of x	evaluation of P(d) at f(x)	82

Name	Program, func-tion, or Com-mand?	Necessary Input	Output	Page
diffq()	Program	None. Program provides 20 subprograms for solving special differential equations	solution to differential equation determined by program input	81
diffshif()	Program	none	program uses a differential shift technique to find a particular solution to a de of the form $P(D)y=e^{\wedge}(ax)$	N/A
difftrig()	Program	none	program uses a differential shift technique to find a particular solution to a de of the form $P(D)y=\sin(ax)$	N/A
dirder(f,pt,abc)	Function	f is a function, pt is a point in the form [x0,y0,z0], and abc is a vector	the directional derivative at the given point in the direction of the vector abc	94-95
DQ(f)	Function	function of x	the difference quotient in terms of x and h	35
dslv1()	Program (called from diffq() program)	None. Program prompts for first order differential equation (with or without initial condition)	solution of differential equation	87
dslv2()	Program (called from diffq() program)	None. Program prompts for second order differential equation (with or without initial conditions)	solution of differential equation	87-88
DV()	Program	None. Upon execution, user is prompted for function and differential order	the triple integral determined by input	64
euler()	Program	None. Upon execution, user is prompted for function f(x,y) point x0,y0 and increment h	approximate solution using Euler's method	N/A
exct(m,n)	Function (called from diffq() program)	m and n where $M(x,y)*dx+N(x,y)*dy=0$	solution to the differential equation	82
expand(	Command	expression	expanded expression	2, 3
factor(	Command	expression, [var]	factored expression (if possible)	2, 3
fmax(	Command	expression,var	value of var that maximizes expression	6
fMin(	Command	expression,var	value of var that minimizes expression	6
fol(p,f)	Function	p and f are based on the first order linear de: $y'+p*y=f$	solution of differential equation	N/A

112

Name	Program, func-tion, or Com-mand?	Necessary Input	Output	Page
fourier()	Program	None. The program prompts for semi-period, # of desired terms, and assumes given function is stored in y1(x).	approximate (finite) Fourier series and its graph (or half-range versions)	103-105
idif(eq,n)	Function	eq is an implicit equation in x and y; n is the order of requested derivative	nth order derivative	43-45
ifactr(m,n)	Function	m and n where M(x,y)*dx+N(x,y)*dy=0	possible integrating factors	N/A
implicit(eq,x,y)	Program	eq is an implicit equation in x and y; x is minimum x window value and y is min y window value	a plot of eq	46
Integrate $\int($	Command	expression,var	indefinite integral	5
Integrate $\int($	Command	expression,var,lower,upper	definite integral	5
lagrange(fn,{var})	Program	vars is a list of variables found in fn a function of the form $f + \lambda g + \mu h$	a list of possible solutions	99-100
limit(	Command	expression,var,value	two-sided limit of expression evaluated at var=value	5
limit(	Command	expression,var,value,a	limit from the right if a is positive and from the left if a is negative	5
lplc(w)	Function	w is a function of t	the Laplace transform of w (as a function of s)	83
minmax(f)	Program	a function of x and y	saddle points, local minima, local maxima	69-70
nDeriv(	Command	expression,var,[h]	numerical derivative [as a function of h]	6
newton()	Program	none	approximation to zero of function	37
Partial(f,{vars})	Function	f is a function of the independent variables; list {vars} is a sequence of partials to be executed	the requested partial derivatives of f	63-64
picard()	Program (called from diffq() program)	None. Program prompts for a 1st order de, initial cond, and # of desired approximations	a series of iterations that approximate the solution	89-90

Name	Program, func-tion, or Com-mand?	Necessary Input	Output	Page
planes()	Program	None	menu driven with choices to find the distance between a point and a line, distance between a point and a plane, the equation of a tangent plane, and the equation of the plane containing three given points	93-94
product $\prod($	Command	expres-sion,var,lower,upper	product of expression from lower to upper	5
proj(A,B)	Function (called from vectdisp())	A and B must be 2- or 3-dimensional vectors	the vector projection of B onto A	93
projctle(a,v,g)	Function	a is the launch angle in radians, v is the launch velocity, g is influence of gravit	flight height, flight time, and flight distance	NA
propFrac(	Command	expression, [var]	proper fraction	4
ptlin(xt,yt,zt,pt)	Function (called from planes() program)	xt, yt, zt are parametric components of vector; pt is a point	the distance the point is from the line	93-94
ptpln(pon,n,poff)	Function (called from planes() program)	pon is a point on the plane, n is the normal vector to the plane and poff is a point off the plane	the distance the point is from the plane	94, 97
reduct(y,p)	Function (called from diffq() pro-gram)	y is a known solution to y"+p(x)*y'+q(x)*y=0	a second solution to y"+p(x)*y'+q(x)*y=0	83
roots(f)	Program (called from diffq() pro-gram)	f is a function of x	no visible output but all the zeros of f (including multiple zeros) are saved in the lo-cation an	N/A
separ()	Program	None	This program is called by diffq() and returns solutions to differential equations that are separable	81
sepsys()	Program (called from diffq() pro-gram)	None	solution of differential equa-tion system when each is in separable form	91
sequence()	Program	None	Prompts the user for gen-eral sequence term and then computes terms and partial sums and provides a sketch	N/A
series()	Program (called from diffq() pro-gram)	None	a series solution to differen-tial equation	N/A

114

Name	Program, function, or Command?	Necessary Input	Output	Page
signl()	Program	None. Program prompts user for function of x, start value and table increment	sign lines for f' and f''	N/A
simperr(err,a,b)	Program	err is a predetermined maximum error, a and b are endpoints	number of subdivisions necessary to insure err (note output must be rounded up to next even integer)	56-57
simpson1(a,b,n)	Program	a is lower bound, b is upper bound and n is the number of subdivisions	graph with parabolic arcs and calculation of area approximation	55-57
solve(	Command	equation, var	solution(s) in a Boolean expression	2, 3, 10
sum $\sum$ (	Command	expression,var,lower,upper	summation of expression from lower to upper	5
sva()	Program	None	distance, velocity, and acceleration values at input endpoints	N/A
tangent(f,a)	Function	f is a function of x; a is x value of point	equation of line drawn tangent to y=f(x) at x=a	33
tanpln(f,x0,y0,z0)	Function (called from planes() program)	f is the function representing the surface (where f(x,y,z)=0) and x0, y0, z0 are the coordinates on the surface to which the desired plane is tangent	the equation of the plane tangent to the given surface at the given point	94, 97
taylor(	Command	expression,var,n,point	the nth order taylor polynomial expression approximation of expression at var=point	6, 59-60
threepts(p1,p2,p3)	Function (called from planes() program)	p1, p2, p3 are three points in space	the equation of the plane containing the three given points	94, 97
tnb(xt,yt,zt)	Program	xt, yt, zt are parametric components of vector	the normal, tangent, and binormal vectors in terms of t stored as a(t), b(t), and c(t), respectively	N/A
tnvector(f)	Program	f is a function of x	the normal and tangent vectors in terms of x with the choice to evaluate at x=a	N/A
totdif()	Program (called from diffq() program)	None. Program prompts user for function of x and y	the total differential of f	85
vecang()	Function (called from vectdisp())	None. Prompts user for two 2- or 3-dimensional vectors	the angle between the vectors	93

Name	Program, function, or Command?	Necessary Input	Output	Page
veccur(f,g)	Function	f and g are functions of x	the angle between the corresponding tangent vectors at x=a	N/A
vecplot(v1,v2)	Program	v1 and v2 are lists containing components of 2-dimensional vectors	plot of the 2-d vectors v1 and v2 as well as their sum	96
vectdisp(v1,v2)	Program	v1 and v2 are either 2- or 3-dimensional vectors	norms of each vector, dot product, cross product and norm, angle between vectors, and project of each onto the other	93
vopgen()	Program (called from diffq() program)	None. Program prompts for an nth order de and solutions to its corresponding homogeneous equation	the particular solution (using variation of parameters)	89
wronskn()	Function (called from diffq() program)	vector of functions of x	value of the Wronskian of the collection	83-84
zeros(	Command	expression, var	list of expression's real zeros	3, 8, 13

NOTES

INDEX

118

differentiation, implicit, 43-46

directional derivative, 94-95, 98

dot product, 93

E

entry, 10

envelope of a solution, 79

equi-dimensional equation, 92

error, in Simpson's rule, 56-57

Euler's formula, 61

exact differential equation, 74, 75, 82

extrema, 69-71

eye perspective in 3D, 24

F

factor, 2-3

first order differential, 73-75, 87

forward difference quotient, 6

Fourier series, 103-108

function

    extrema, 6, 69-71

    piecewise smooth, 107

    maximum of, 6

Fundamental Theorem of Calculus, 49-53

G

Gradient, 94-95, 98

graph <-> table, 13

graph formats, 7

graph style

    animate, 17

    path, 17

graphing/graphs

    differential equations, 7-9, 25-26

    grids, 8

    of implicit functions, 44

    intersection of, 9-10

    parametric equation, 16-17

    pause while, 13

    polar equations, 17-19

    sequences, 20-22

    3D, 22-24, 70

grids, 8

H

half-range expansion, 107

hidden surface, 21-22

homogeneous differential equations, 75

I

implicit differentiation, 43-46

implicit multiplication, 3

inflection point, 12

integral(s), 4-5, 51-52

    multiple, 64-65

integrating factor, 74

integration, 11

intersection of two graphs, 9-10

interval of convergence, 62

Other Books of Interest

Exploring Precalculus with the TI-89, TI-92, and TI-92 Plus by Michael Schneider and Lawrence Gilligan (1999)
ISBN: 1-888808-04-7

The TI-86/85 Reference Guide by Nelson Rich and Lawrence Gilligan (1997)
ISBN: 1-888808-01-2

Diskette of 34 programs to accompany the *TI-86/85 Reference Guide* by Michael Schneider (1997)
ISBN (PC Format): 1-888808-03-9 ISBN (Mac Format): 1-888808-02-0

Mastering the TI-92: Explorations from Algebra through Calculus by Nelson Rich, Judith Rose, and Lawrence Gilligan (1996)
ISBN: 0-9626661-9-x

Calculus and the DERIVE® Program: Experiments with the Computer, 3rd Edition by Lawrence Gilligan and James Marquardt (1995)
ISBN: 0-9626661-8-1

The TI-85 Reference Guide by Nelson Rich and Lawrence Gilligan (1993)
ISBN: 0-9626661-6-5

Linear Algebra Experiments Using the DERIVE® Program by Mary Salter and Lawrence Gilligan (1992)
ISBN: 0-9626661-4-9

For descriptions of all the titles on the previous page, announcements of new titles, and special offers, check us out on the internet:

http://www.gilmarpublishing.com

Email: gilmar2000@yahoo.com